Radio Position Fixing
for Yachtsmen

Radio Position Fixing for Yachtsmen

AN INTRODUCTION TO DECCA, LORAN, OMEGA AND TRANSIT

CLAUD POWELL
CEng FIERE FRIN

ADLARD COLES LIMITED
8 Grafton Street, London W1

Adlard Coles Ltd
William Collins Sons & Co. Ltd
8 Grafton Street, London W1X 3LA

First published in Great Britain by
Adlard Coles Ltd 1987

British Library Cataloguing in Publication Data
Powell, Claud
Radio position fixing for yachtsmen: an
introduction to Decca, Loran, Omega and
Transit.
1. Radio in navigation   2. Yachts and
yachting.   3. Radio frequency
I. Title
623.89'32   VK560

ISBN 0-229-11788-0

Printed and bound in Great Britain
Mackays of Chatham Ltd, Kent

Contents

1   Hyperbolic Position Lines, 1

Beginnings. Hyperbolic position lines. Why hyperbolic? The hyperbola. The position line pattern. Some characteristics. Position line divergence. Types of position line error. Basis of fixed errors. Homing. Summary.

2   The Position Fix, 12

Introduction. Angle of cut. Angle between baselines. The star chain. The position fix. Fixed errors. Variable errors. Drms and Dwf. Probability. Repeatability. Rendezvous accuracy. Examine the lattice. Scale of the systems. Summary.

3   Waves, Lanes and Pulses, 22

Introduction. Radio waves. Phase and phase difference. Use of continuous waves. The lane. Ambiguity. Lane identification. Effect of receiver movement. Sorting out the signals. Use of pulses. Why the two techniques? Groundwave and skywave. Monitor stations. Effects of weather. The on-board installation. Summary.

9 Navigation Facilities, 77

Introduction. Latitude and longitude. Warning indications. Discrepancies between receivers. Different co-ordinates, same fix. Geodetic datum. The Ghost Buoy. Waypoint definition. Waypoint storage. Position marking. Waypoints as marker buoys. Calibrated waypoints. Steering to a waypoint. Route marking. Change of leg direction. Steering note. Autopilots. Track and speed made good. Dead reckoning. Time-related displays. Take care. Dummy run.

Illustrations

Chapter 5

Chapter 6

Chapter 7

Chapter 9

Foreword

M. W. RICHEY MBE
Director, the Royal Institute of Navigation, 1947–83

The problem of position remains central to navigation, which for this purpose we may define as the whole business of conducting a craft from one place to another. For the last two or three hundred years the standard way of solving this at sea offshore has been by astronomical navigation; obtaining position lines by timed observations of heavenly bodies. The standard method nowadays is by the measurement of radio waves, using position fixing systems such as Decca, Loran-C, Omega or, more recently, satellites. All these aids are now available to small craft at a cost which might be considered reasonable in relation to other equipment. (Whether they are necessary is a matter for the individual owner.)

When astronomical navigation was the standard method, the navigator was expected to know just what he was doing when he took a sight and used the nautical almanac and reduction tables to derive a position line. He would understand the navigational triangle, the concepts of declination and hour angle, the relationship between time and longitude, the effect of astronomical and terrestrial refraction on altitude, and so on: he would, in short, have a grasp of the elements of nautical astronomy. He could thus be expected to appreciate the sources of error and the reliability of his observations. No such standard of education seems to be required of those who use electronic methods to establish position; and yet they are desirable for precisely similar reasons.

Claud Powell's book admirably performs in relation to hyperbolic navigation the functions of the classic navigation manual of an earlier era. It is not a book about equipment but about the principles underlying the various position fixing systems and their application in the equipment currently (or prospectively) available. It is written, with great lucidity, for the navigator (and especially the navigator of small craft) in language with which he will be familiar, entirely free from jargon of any kind. As one would expect of an author with so distinguished a background, the treatment of every subject is navigationally impeccable.

Some of us in our recreational sailing remain obdurately opposed to hi-tech navigation, preferring to exercise the traditional skills. That must remain a matter of choice. The more enlightened who take advantage of the systems available should benefit greatly from this book which should lead to a more discerning and discriminate use of the equipment.

Yacht *Jester*
October 1986

Preface

The aim of this book is to introduce in non-technical fashion, with the navigation of small craft in mind, the principles and characteristics of hyperbolic position fixing and of the navigational aids that provide it: the Decca Navigator, Loran-C and Omega. Position fixing by means of the Transit navigation-satellite system is also described. My hope is that the background information in these pages will help to give first-time users a 'feel' for how the systems work and for their possibilities and limitations.

There is no reference to electronics as such but some attention is given to the properties of radio waves. Individual items of equipment are not described because at the present rate of progress such material would too soon need updating, and in my view the proper source of practical information on any equipment is the relevant *Users' Manual*.

The 'yachtsmen' in the title are persons who cruise in coastal waters or on the high seas, whether under sail or power or both, for pleasure rather than professionally. In the USA they are described more comprehensively as 'recreational boaters'.

C.P.
October 1986

Acknowledgements

I am grateful to the following individuals and organisations for their help: Rear Admiral R. M. Burgoyne, CB, Director of the Royal Institute of Navigation, for permission to reproduce illustrations (Figs. 1 and 24) from the *Journal of Navigation*; Mr A. D. Wheeler, Technical Director of Racal-Decca Marine Navigation Ltd, for permission to reproduce illustrations from company publications (Figs. 4, 11, 14, 17, 19–22, 23, 25–28, 30, 31, 35); Mr P. Comyns, Sales Manager of Greenham Marine Ltd, for information on Loran-C and other equipment; and Mr A. G. Johns, Technical Director of Walker's Marine Instruments, for information on hyperbolic and Transit equipment and for comments on installation and operation topics.

Finally my thanks are due to Captain N. H. Keeler, Chief of the Radionavigation Division, United States Coast Guard, for information supplied including back issues of the USCG *Radionavigation Bulletin*, and to Commander R. J. Wenzel of US Coast Guard Activities, Europe (ACTEUR), for replies to my questions by letter and telephone.

1
Hyperbolic Position Lines

Beginnings

Somewhere in the United States, towards the end of the last century, a (then) revolutionary proposal for a navigational aid was tried out on board a small steamship. A report is known to have been published but has so far proved untraceable; the object, however, was to discover whether a straight channel could be marked by means of sound-signals in place of lights or buoys. Two powerful electrically-operated bells had been sited symmetrically either side of the channel, about half a mile apart, and were connected by a cable so that they would ring simultaneously when an operator on shore pressed a button.

In this test the operator was giving a short ring every few seconds. On the open bridge of the ship, the helmsman and a group of observers were listening intently to determine whether the sounds of the bells (which were of different pitch) were arriving exactly together. If so, they knew the ship was on track but if, say, the port-hand bell was heard first the helmsman would alter course to starboard... and so on. The scheme was not adopted operationally, possibly because the bells were difficult to hear in any but calm weather, but its use of synchronised signals from separate transmitters to generate a line of position foreshadowed the navigational aids described in this book.

The scene changes to an army proving-ground in Europe, and the year to 1912. Three artillery officers are synchronising their watches, which are the best that money can buy. Great care is being taken to synchronise them as accurately as possible. This done, the officers ride off to take up their respective positions at three points spaced about a kilometre apart. The points, marked by flags, have been accurately surveyed beforehand and plotted on a large-scale map of the area.

Here the object is to discover whether it would be possible to determine the position of a field gun fired somewhere in the locality, by comparing the times at which the sound of its report arrived at the three known points. If it worked this would be a breakthrough in artillery warfare since it would allow an enemy gun or battery to be engaged 'unseen'. In due course the test gun is fired and each observer logs the exact time at which he heard it. After repeating the test to get average figures, they return to HQ to plot the results. There the map showing the observing-points A, B, and C (Fig.1) has been overprinted with lines

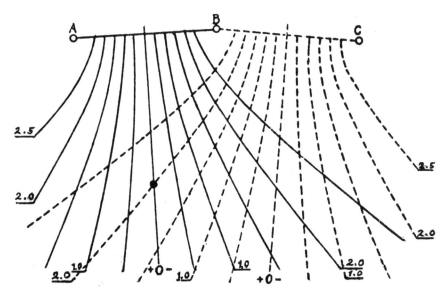

Fig. 1 Time difference grid for locating an enemy gun.
(From a German Army document of 1918.)

on which the gun would theoretically lie, given a value for the speed of sound, if pairs of observers had heard it at times differing by 0, 0.5, 1.0 (etc.) seconds.

Comparing their results, the observers who had been at points A and B found they had recorded identical times, indicating that the gun must lie somewhere on the solid line marked +0−. The time recorded at C, however, was 2 seconds later than at B, so the gun must also lie on the dotted +2.0 line. The exercise had thus fixed the gun's position on the map at the point where the two lines cross. History does not relate how accurate this position fix was, but 'sound ranging' became highly effective once suitable microphones and timers had been developed.

The sound ranging experiment goes a long way towards explaining how today's hyperbolic radio position fixing systems work. They are so called because of the geometrical form of the position lines, of which those in Fig. 1 are examples. The time differences in which the radio systems deal are of course very much smaller, since radio waves travel about a million times faster than sound, and the radio systems work 'the other way round': the known points are occupied by synchronised transmitting stations and the unknown position by the user's receiver.

Hyperbolic position lines

In this chapter the construction and characteristics of a position-line pattern are outlined, with reference to general principles rather than to any particular system. Most of the features described are common to Decca and Loran, despite the technical differences between the two systems, and in principle to Omega also, although its large dimensions tend for various reasons to set it apart. The term 'time difference' (TD) will be used to denote the basic measurement performed by the on-board receiver. In the Loran system the TD is displayed in microseconds while with Decca and Omega it is reckoned in the 'lanes' described in Chapter 3. Hyperbolic position lines are often referred to as LOPs (lines of position).

Most of the on-board receivers used with these systems, and especially those for pleasure craft, transform the hyperbolic position fix into latitude/longitude and waypoint data. This does not in any way affect the characteristics of the hyperbolic fix, however – an important point which is mentioned again in Chapter 9.

Why hyperbolic?

It is worth noting at the outset what hyperbolic position fixing has to offer that could not be supplied by, say, radio direction-finding (D/F) or by the range and bearing to a known position that an on-board radar can provide. Hyperbolic fixing has three main advantages: it is inherently more accurate than any normal form of D/F; it provides a continuous fix so long as the stations are within range; and (unlike position fixing systems based on range measurement) it does not require the user craft to transmit radio signals. Confining transmission to the shore stations allows any number of craft to use the service simultaneously. These features combine to put the hyperbolic systems in a class of their own.

The hyperbola

The constant-time-difference curves in Fig.1 were based on a known value for the speed of sound. It follows that at all points on a given curve there is a constant difference in the distance to two fixed points (such as A and B); by that definition the curve is a hyperbola. The word comes from two Greek words identifying the section of a cone that results when the cone is cut by a plane at an angle that is 'excessively thrown' beyond a certain limit. For further details refer to any maths book covering the theory of Conic Sections.

While everyone can see that a curve on which all points are equidistant from a fixed point is a circle, and that points in the same direction from a fixed point lie on a straight line, the shape of a line along which the distance-difference to two fixed points is constant is not so easy to visualise. Even so, the construction of such lines is simple and needs nothing more than drawing instruments, patience, and a willingness to assume for the time being that the earth is flat. Drawing instruments have been devised that will generate a hyperbola in one 'shot', although these now have only curiosity value. Users of the hyperbolic navigation systems are not required to draw hyperbolas, but knowledge of their construction is the key to understanding how the systems work.

The position line pattern

Suppose a radio transmitter at a known position T (Fig.2) radiates a single short burst or pulse of energy. Assuming that this signal travels at a constant speed, its outward progress may be depicted on a map as a set of circles centred on the station. The spacing between the circles is equal to the distance the signal travels in a certain time; taking the 'propagation' speed as 300 metres per microsecond (a convenient approximation to the speed of light and radio waves) and drawing the

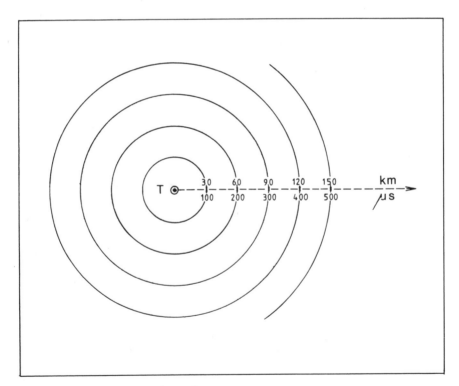

Fig. 2 Propagation of a radio pulse.
Circles represent the propagation of the signal from transmitter T in space and time, at a speed of 300 metres per microsecond.

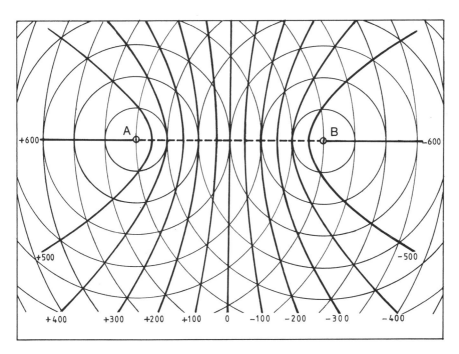

Fig. 3 Construction of a hyperbolic pattern.
Time differences (B–A) are in μs and assume simultaneous transmission
from A and B. Baseline AB = 180 km, propagation speed 300 m/μs.

circles to represent time increments of 100 μs, the circles will be 30 km
apart in the diagram.

Two such signals are represented in the same way in Fig.3,
transmitted from separate stations at known positions A and B, and it is
assumed that the two pulses leave their respective antennas at the same
instant. To establish a pattern of lines along which the arrival-time of the
A and B signals will differ by a constant value it is only necessary to
draw smooth curves connecting the intersection points of the circles, as
shown by the thick lines. The result is known as a hyperbolic pattern.
(In practice the synchronised transmissions are repeated at some
convenient rate, to give continuity, but the rate has no effect on the
shape of the curves and we can therefore ignore it.)

Knowing the station positions and the propagation speed, the
pattern can be overprinted on a map or chart and the lines labelled with
the TD values. An on-board receiver that measures and displays the TD
will thus identify on the chart a position-line passing through the craft.
The diagram is of course a 'blackboard illustration' of how hyperbolas
are constructed and production of the actual charts has to take earth
curvature and other factors into account. The lines in Fig.3 are
numbered in the very logical way used in Fig.1, although in practice the

Decca, Loran and Omega systems have numbering schemes of their own.

Some characteristics

Foremost among the characteristics of a hyperbolic position line is its potentially high accuracy compared, say, with that of a bearing obtained on a conventional D/F set. A position line accuracy of 20 m at a range of 200 km from the baseline midpoint is not unusual for Loran or Decca and this corresponds to a bearing accuracy more than 100 times higher than that of D/F at its best. The accuracy of the TD measurement is, however, affected in one way or another by many different factors, but

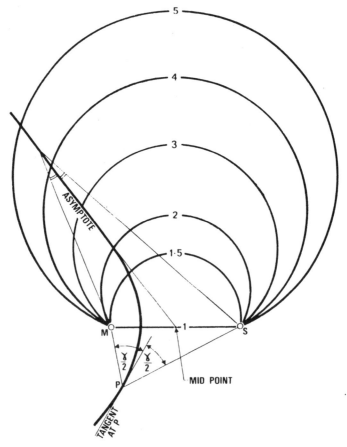

Fig. 4 Properties of a hyperbolic pattern.
   Contours for expansion factors 1–5 are shown. At any point P the tangent to the hyperbola bisects angle MPS. At a distance, a hyperbola coincides with a straight line through the midpoint of the baseline. Scale of the diagram is given by the baseline length MS.

before considering these it is helpful to look at the position line pattern more closely.

First it should be noted in Fig.3 that although the concentric circles are spaced to represent time increments of 100 μs in the outward progress of the signal, and so are 30 km apart, the time-difference lines labelled, say, +200 and +300 are only 15 km apart measured along the baseline AB. This is simply because a change of position of 15 km along the baseline towards A entails moving the same distance away from B and makes a total change of 30 km in the distance-difference.

It will be seen that the pattern contains three straight lines: the central zero-difference line and the two baseline extensions beyond A and B. On either baseline extension, the difference in the distances to A and B is of course equal to AB. In Fig.4 it is shown that as distance from the stations increases, the hyperbolas become coincident with (asymptotic to) straight lines passing through the midpoint of the baseline. Use was made of this characteristic in the now obsolete Consol system, in which a hyperbolic pattern was generated on a very short baseline such that the position lines were curved only in the immediate neighbourhood of the transmitting antenna system. Elsewhere they were virtually straight and were treated as radials originating at the centre of the baseline.

The same drawing also shows that at any point, the tangent to a hyperbola bisects the angle subtended at that point by the baseline: this is of more than just academic interest since it enables one to estimate, knowing the station positions, the direction in which the position line at a given spot will run.

Position line divergence

The characteristic divergence of the lines in a hyperbolic pattern is known as the lane expansion (the UK term) or gradient (USA). The extent to which the position line will be displaced by a given TD error depends upon where the receiver is located in the pattern, and is minimum – and constant – at all points on the baseline joining the stations. In contrast, on or near the baseline extensions the pattern is relatively 'insensitive' to changes of position, as can be seen in Fig.3, and it also becomes less sensitive as distance from the stations is increased in any direction.

Curves of constant expansion factor or gradient, for five different values, are shown in Fig.4. The scale is given by whatever length is assigned to the baseline and each curve shows the area within which any error in the TD reading will be multiplied, considered in terms of distance, by the factor indicated. In other words a given TD error would displace the position line four times farther from the true position if the receiver were located on curve 4 than if it were located on the baseline.

Types of position line error

The TD that the on-board receiver displays can be in error through radio propagation effects, interference by noise, imperfections in the equipment, and other causes. There are two kinds of error: those which vary randomly with time, making them unpredictable in value except on a statistical basis, and those which remain fixed with time although they may vary from place to place. Random errors are in general the more important and their effect upon the position fix, which of course combines the errors in two position lines, is described in the next chapter. A fixed error can by definition be corrected once its value has

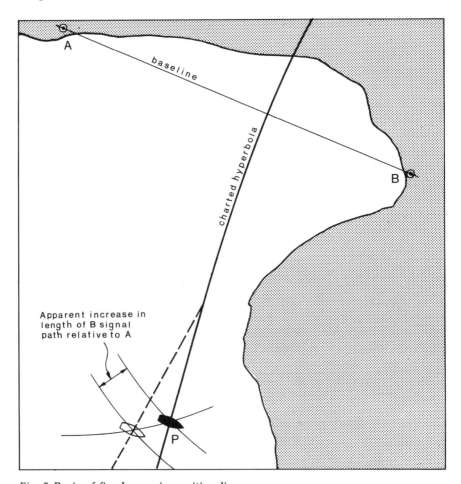

Fig. 5 Basis of fixed error in position line.
At position P the signal from station B is delayed by passing over land. Here this decreases the observed TD, causing an error in the displayed LOP. Dotted line shows (exaggerated) the permanent distortion of the hyperbola due to the land path.

been determined by observation and made known to users of the system. Fixed errors are described as such in the case of Decca but are termed 'additional secondary phase factors' (ASF) for Loran and Omega.

Basis of fixed errors

An error that exists at a given location but remains fixed with time, so that its value is the same for every receiver-equipped craft visiting that spot, is the result of a breakdown of the assumption that radio waves travel at a known and constant speed. For example, in Fig.5 the ship is at a location to which the signal from B travels largely over land. A long land path, particularly if it consists of terrain of low electrical conductivity such as rock or desert, has the effect of slowing down the propagation speed compared with the speed over sea-water. There will thus be an apparent increase in the distance to B and the TD will identify a position line displaced in the direction shown.

This is a simplified approach to an often complex effect but at least the diagram indicates the probable sense of the error in the case of a single over-land path. As land is approached, and particularly inshore, fixed error values can differ significantly at points only a few hundred feet apart. In an estuary, for example, it pays to observe the TD readings at as many fixed points as possible rather than assume that a single observation will hold good over a large area around that point.

Homing

When a hyperbolic position line happens to coincide with a required track, that track can be made good simply by steering so that the receiver LOP readout (if provided) continues to display the TD value of the selected line (Fig.6). The TD would be obtained from a chart or from previous observation. If the readout deviates above or below that TD, the helmsman alters course in a direction that will depend on that of the pattern numbering. Originally known as homing, this procedure results in the highest accuracy of track-keeping that Loran or Decca can achieve since it is subject only to the error in the single position line that coincides with the required track. (In general Omega has insufficient basic accuracy to be used in this way.) Fishermen, in particular, employ homing for track keeping and as a means of recovering a particular position as accurately as possible.

The TD reading itself does not of course provide any information of a directional character. In homing, all it shows – within the accuracy of the system – is whether the craft's receiving antenna is located on the

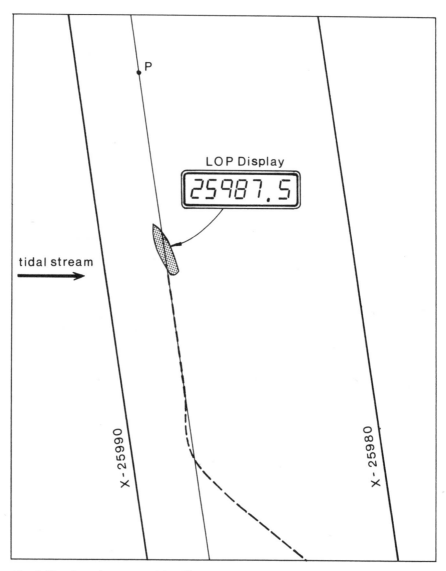

Fig. 6 Homing along a position line.
To make good a track coincident with a specified LOP (here Loran X-25987.5) and/or to recover a position P known to lie on that LOP, steer a compass course such that the displayed TD remains constant at the required reading.

required track or, if not, how far off-track it is in terms of TD units, and to which side. (It is possible in principle, although seldom advisable or necessary, to change the craft's heading by 180° without this affecting the TD at all.) The compass, with its sensitivity to small changes in heading, remains indispensable and homing entails the judicious use of the compass and the TD readout together, especially when there is a cross-tide.

Summary

The difference in the arrival-time of synchronised signals from a pair of separate transmitters locates the receiver on a hyperbolic line of position. The TD is measured directly in time units or indirectly in other units, depending on the system. There is nothing complicated about a hyperbola except perhaps the word itself. The graphical construction of a hyperbolic pattern could hardly be simpler, and helps to explain the principle. Although potentially accurate, hyperbolic position lines are subject to errors or variations. A single position line can be a useful aid to accurate track-keeping.

2
The Position Fix

Introduction

The lattice or grid formed by two hyperbolic patterns was introduced in Fig.1, and is shown again in Fig.7 where one pattern is generated by synchronised radio transmitting stations A and B and the other similarly by A and C. The common station is known as the master and the others as slaves (Decca) or secondary stations (Loran). Omega stations are not regarded as having a master/slave relationship, as explained in Chapter 6, although their synchronisation is no less essential than with the other

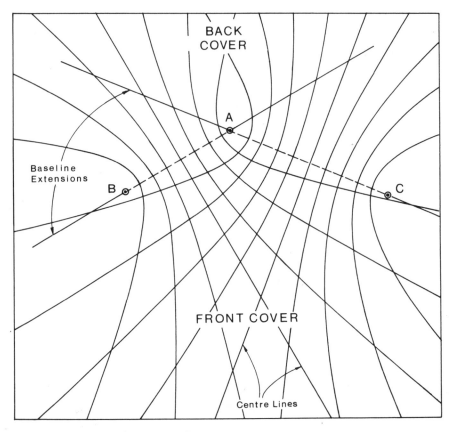

Fig. 7 Lattice produced by station pairs AB, AC.

systems. With each of the systems a fix is sometimes obtained from two separate baselines, i.e. from four stations, but the common-master arrangement is more generally used.

The on-board receiver measures the time difference between the arrival of the A and B signals and, independently, the TD between the arrival of the A and C signals. How it sorts out the different signals is left to the next chapter, as are the details of how Loran measures the TD directly in microseconds whereas Decca and Omega deal in other units. We shall also continue to assume that the receiver simply displays the TDs as numerical LOP readings which the user plots by hand in the correspondingly-numbered lattice on his chart; the intersection-point of the two lines thus identified is the craft's position.

Lattice charts are published in a wide range of scales and only a few are of small enough scale to include one or more of the station positions. Those for marine use are generally charts which are also published in un-latticed form and which have been overprinted with the lattice by the hydrographic or cartographic authority of the country concerned. Since there is a limit to the number of lines that can be printed, a TD reading will more often than not refer to a line which is not printed and which the user finds by interpolation between the nearest printed lines on either side.

Angle of cut

Setting aside radio-related factors such as variations in signal propagation, signal/noise conditions, etc., the accuracy of the position fix depends mainly on the expansion or gradient of the patterns and the angle of cut (the UK term) or crossing angle (USA) between the two position-lines from which the fix is obtained. Except for the special case of baselines at 180° the combined effect of expansion and angle of cut gives lower accuracy in the 'back cover' than in the front. This can be seen in Figs 7 and 8.

In the front cover of a three-station chain the angle of cut reaches 90°. The locus of points where the angle of cut is 90° is the straight line joining the outer stations B and C: the key to proving this is the property of the tangent to a hyperbola noted in Fig.4. Elsewhere the angle of cut decreases with distance from the stations until at very long ranges it virtually vanishes and the fix degenerates into a single position line.

Angle between baselines

In the three-station layout the angle between the baselines has a strong effect upon how the distance and direction of the receiver from the

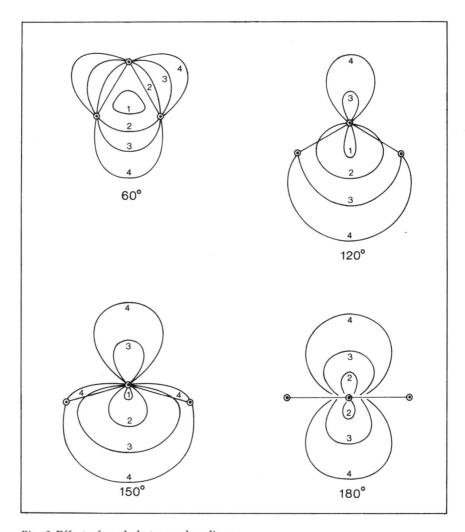

Fig. 8 Effect of angle between baselines.
Contours 1–4 represent four arbitrary levels of position fixing accuracy. The diagrams have a common scale and assume the same level of random error in the TDs.

stations affects the accuracy of the fix. This is worth noting because, owing to the often great difficulty of obtaining suitable sites for the stations, hyperbolic chains vary widely in angular configuration as well as in baseline-length. In Fig.8 four different baseline angles are shown, together with approximate contours indicating the areas within which four levels of accuracy 1, 2, 3, and 4, will be available. In each case the inner contour (1) indicates the area where accuracy is highest.

The star chain

It will be seen that a baseline angle of 120° gives about the best compromise between accuracy and coverage area. This makes the 'star' configuration of Fig.9 an economical layout for a Decca or Loran chain. The layout does not have to be symmetrical nor the baseline lengths equal. The three patterns of a star chain combine to cover a roughly circular area around the master station, using a dovetailing combination of front and back cover as in Fig.9. A few Decca chains provide only two patterns and some Loran chains have four. Omega is regarded as a single global chain.

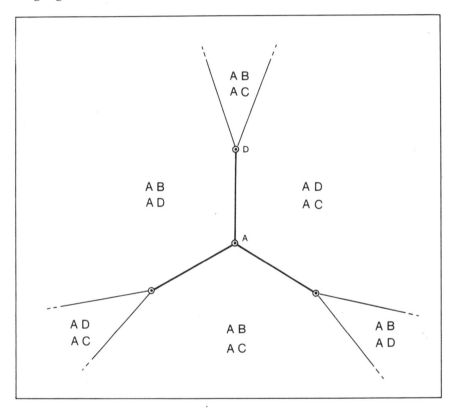

Fig. 9 All-round coverage of star chain.

The position fix

Although a star chain provides three patterns of position lines, the normal practice when plotting the fix is to use the two that cut at the best angle, and discard the third. For this reason lattice charts (particularly those for Decca) seldom carry more than the two patterns to be used. An attempt to form a cocked hat by adding a third position line would generally tend to increase the error of the fix, especially if the receiver happened to be located near a baseline-extension of the third pattern, unless a rather elaborate weighting procedure is adopted. A processor can do this, with a level of success that depends to some extent on how much skywave interference (see next chapter) is present and some modern receivers include a position fixing mode using all three patterns.

Fixed errors

These were discussed in the previous chapter and may be present in either or both of the position lines used. It should be noted however that when the signal from the common master station travels over a long and/or low-conductivity land path to a given spot, this is likely to produce a fixed error in each of the position lines at that spot. Details of how data on fixed errors are promulgated to users are given in the chapters on the respective systems, but users can of course make their own observations of the fixed error at points of interest whose position is known. Some lattice charts for Loran incorporate corrections for observed fixed error values.

Variable errors

Some level of variation will be present in the receiver's measurement of the TDs, even under good conditions, and the prevailing level of random error is generally the factor that sets the limit to the accuracy and/or range obtainable. The relationship between the variations in the position lines and the resulting uncertainty in the position fix are illustrated in Fig.10. The fix may fall anywhere within the shaded 'error diamond', an idea which is not peculiar to hyperbolic systems and which applies whenever a fix is formed from two position lines that are subject to variations. Near the stations the diamond compresses almost to a square but as the distance increases it becomes larger and more elongated, as shown by the two insets to the drawing.

Drms and Dwf

The published figures for the predicted level of position fixing accuracy are generally expressed in terms of the root-mean-square error (Drms), the basis of which is shown in Fig.11. Drms is expressed in units of distance (hence the D) and is equal to the radius of a circle centred on the true position. This radius is in turn related to the ellipse which in theory

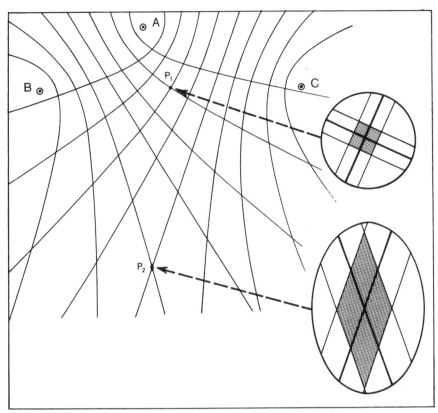

Fig. 10 Effect of range upon accuracy.
The two insets are drawn to the same scale. Shading represents the uncertainty in the position fix at points P1 and P2 for the same level of random error in the TDs.

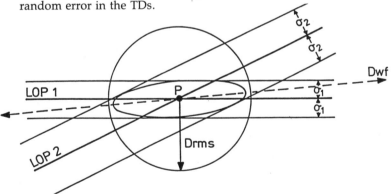

Fig. 11 Error ellipse, Drms and Dwf.
σ_1, σ_2 are the standard deviations of the TDs at the true position P and are assumed here to be uncorrelated. Drms = $\sqrt{a^2 + b^2}$ where a and b are the half-axes (not shown) of the error ellipse, and is represented as the radius of a circle centred on the true position. The direction of worst fix, Dwf, coincides with the major axis of the ellipse, and approximately with the bisector of the angle of cut.

will be formed by the spread or scatter of successive fixes observed at a given spot owing to the variations in the position lines.

Drms is a conservative rating in the sense that it takes no account of the higher accuracy that will be obtainable in directions other than the 'direction of worst fix' (Dwf). The latter term is self-explanatory and it can be estimated for any position by a glance at the lattice chart. The full derivation of Drms has to take into account the degree of correlation between the errors in the two position lines, but its basis as shown in Fig.11 should always be borne in mind when using a hyperbolic system.

Most modern receivers display on demand the Drms computed for the present position of the craft, taking into account the effects of time and season when these are applicable (as they are with Decca), together with the Dwf. As explained in Chapter 9, such displays are particularly important when position is being displayed in terms of lat/long or waypoint bearing/distance. Some receivers display an accuracy figure based on the long half-axis of the error diamond and this is sometimes referred to, inappropriately, as the Gdop (geometrical dilution of precision), a term which serves simply to describe the combined effect of gradient and crossing-angle.

Probability

When a system of measurement is subject to random variations, its accuracy can only be specified realistically in terms of some stated level of probability. The notion of probability invokes in turn that of statistics and from the beginning it has been the practice to express the accuracy of hyperbolic navigation systems in statistical terms, on the basis of the predicted Standard Deviation of the TDs.

Subject to certain conditions we can say that if 100 readings are taken of some randomly varying quantity, 68 of these would theoretically be expected to deviate from the mean value of the readings by an amount not exceeding the Standard Deviation. Thus if the position line variations in Fig. 11 are taken to be the Standard Deviations of the TDs, the odds against a plot falling outside the circle will be 2:1.

Published accuracy data on hyperbolic chains are generally based either on the predicted Standard Deviation of the TD variations or on twice the Standard Deviation (i.e. on the one-sigma or two-sigma probability level). If in Fig.11 the levels of the variations were doubled to represent the two-sigma probability, this would double the predicted Drms and according to probability theory the circle would then contain 95% of the plots. Data on Drms are generally published in the form of accuracy contours for individual chains, as an entirely separate exercise from the promulgation of data on fixed or secondary phase errors as defined earlier. The concept of Drms takes no account of errors that remain fixed with time.

Repeatability

Figures for position fixing accuracy that are based on the predicted level of random error are a measure of the repeatability to be expected, that is to say the consistency with which the same TD readings will be obtained on successive visits to a given spot. By definition, a fixed error at that spot would not affect the repeatability.

Rendezvous accuracy

When two vessels are employing the same position fixing system, the accuracy with which one of them can use it to recover a position reported by the other is known as the rendezvous accuracy. If the respective receivers are of different makes or types, rendezvous accuracy can be adversely affected, particularly if the positions are displayed in terms of latitude and longitude rather than as the 'raw' LOPs (see Chapter 9). On the other hand, and particularly in the case of Omega, the accuracy in the rendezvous mode can be good because the correlation between the LOP variations displayed by separate receivers becomes higher as the distance between them decreases (i.e. the variations, even though quite large, tend to cancel out).

Examine the lattice

The user of a hyperbolic system should make a practice of noting the characteristics of the lattice along his intended track. The importance of this advice is illustrated in Fig.12. The lattice chart indicates the Dwf at a glance, everywhere in the area it covers, and for this reason alone its presence on board is a cost-effective investment in safety regardless of whether the receiver in use does or does not display the actual LOP values.

Scale of the systems

The hyperbolic lattice characteristics described in this chapter apply in principle to Decca, Loran and Omega alike. The three systems differ widely in scale, however, and this affects the extent to which the geometrical conditions are liable to change as a voyage proceeds. Most

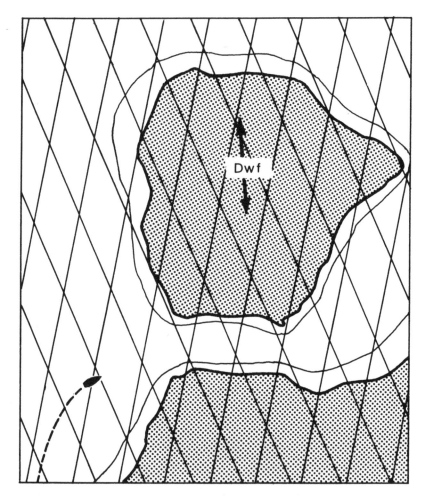

Fig. 12 Watch it ...
Examine the lattice before using position fixes for track keeping.

Decca baselines are less than 100 miles long and the geometrical quality of the coverage of a given chain can change from good to bad in the course of a few hours' sailing. Loran baselines are several hundred miles long and the changes are more gradual, but even so (to quote a United States Coast Guard publication), 'you should be wary of a fix where the LOPs cross at an angle less than 30°'. Omega lattice geometry changes relatively little over very large areas.

Summary

A hyperbolic chain consists of a central master station with two or more outlying slave or secondary stations, generating two or more overlapping patterns of position lines. When manually plotting a fix from a star chain only two LOPs are used, but a processor-based receiver can use three. Published data on fix repeatability are predicted statistically. Correction data are published for fixed errors where these have been measured. Most receivers display an accuracy prediction related to the present position. The geometrical quality of the position fix varies widely over the coverage of a chain and the user should be aware of the lattice characteristics on his intended track.

3
Waves, Lanes and Pulses

Introduction

So far it has been sufficient to assume that a hyperbolic pattern is generated by two stations simultaneously transmitting a pulse-type signal: the radio equivalent of a gun's report. Beyond mentioning, rather obviously, that such signals would have to be repeated at some convenient rate in order to give continuity to the system, nothing has been said about the signals themselves. This will now be remedied but it will be helpful to look first at the continuous-wave (cw) radio transmissions of the kind used by Decca and Omega and then return to the pulse-type signal.

Radio waves

In Fig. 13 the basis of a radio wave is illustrated by arrows which represent the rise of the signal to (say) a positive peak voltage, its fall

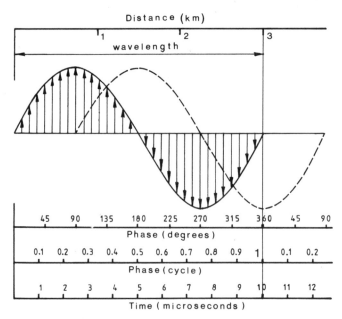

Fig. 13 Properties of a radio wave.
(Frequency f = 100 kHz, propagation speed C = 300 m/μs, wavelength λ = 3.0 km.)

through zero to a negative peak, and then back to zero. The distance that the signal travels during this complete sequence or cycle is termed the wavelength, generally quoted in metres. The cycle repeats itself at a certain frequency, reckoned in cycles per second (Hz) or kHz or MHz as the case may be. (Hz commemorates the German physicist Heinrich Hertz who demonstrated the radiation of radio waves in 1888.)

Frequency and wavelength are so related that

$$f = C/\lambda$$

where f is the frequency in Hz,
    λ is the wavelength in metres, and
    C is the speed of signal propagation in metres per second.

For C a round-figure value of 300 million m/s (300 m/μs) can be accepted here, so for a transmitted frequency of 100 kHz the wavelength would be 3 km, as in Fig.13.

Phase and phase difference

The state that a wave has reached at a given point in the cycle is known as its phase, traditionally measured in degrees since the repetition of the successive cycles is analogous to rotation (hence the word 'cycle'). Phase is clearly time-related and it is by comparing the phase of the two signals involved that a Decca or Omega receiver determines the TD and thus identifies a hyperbolic position line. In Fig.13 there is a phase difference of 90 $^\circ$ or 0.25 cycle between the solid and dotted waves; if the frequency is 100 kHz this difference in phase will be equivalent to a time difference of 2.5 μs.

The necessary synchronism between the signals from the two stations to produce a hyperbolic pattern is achieved by phase-locking them, meaning that the signal from one of the stations is held always in an exact and fixed phase relationship with that from the other. This relationship may have any value so long as it remains constant, but for convenience it is assumed in Fig.14 that the two signals are transmitted with a phase difference of zero ('in phase').

Use of continuous waves

A pair of stations radiating cw signals are shown at M and S in Fig.14. The letters refer to the phase-locking of the slave S to the master M. Here the circles, frozen in time, represent the progress of the signals through successive wavelengths (except the smallest circles: the draughtsman has caught the signals at an instant when they were half-way through a cycle at the transmitters, not that this affects the resulting hyperbolic pattern in any way).

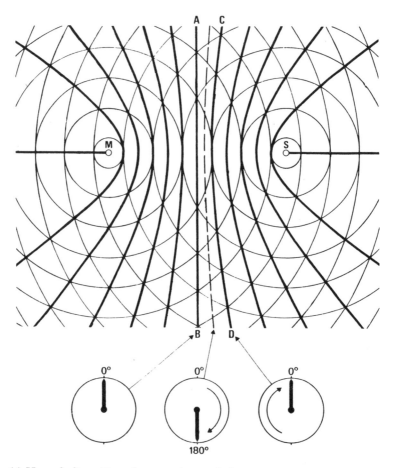

Fig. 14 Hyperbolic pattern from cw transmissions.
Showing response of phase-difference meter to movement from AB to CD.

Below the pattern is an elementary phase-difference meter which, if it were the readout of an on-board receiver located anywhere on the centre-line AB of the pattern, would read 0 as shown. This is because at all points on AB – and indeed on each of the thick lines – the signals arrive in phase.

The lane

Suppose the ship moves away from AB towards station S. This will shorten the distance to S, causing the phase of the signal received from S to advance; at the same time the phase of the M signal will be retarded, since that signal now has farther to travel. The meter will therefore no longer read zero. When the ship reaches the dotted hyperbola where, as can be seen by examining the rings, the signals arrive exactly out-of-phase, the pointer will have turned through 180 degrees (0.5 cycle).

If the voyage continues in the same direction the pointer will eventually make a complete rotation, indicating that the ship has reached the next in-phase line, CD. The direction in which the meter turns for a given direction of movement through the pattern is an arbitrary matter: here the Decca convention is followed of clockwise meter rotation for movement from master to slave. In crossing the space between AB and CD the ship is said to have passed through one *lane*. AB, CD and the other thick lines in the drawing are known as lane boundaries. Measured along the baseline, the lane-width is constant and equal to half a wavelength at the frequency at which phase is compared.

It is sometimes found puzzling that the lane-width on the baseline, corresponding to one whole revolution of the phase-difference meter, should be a half and not one wavelength. In moving along the baseline through one lane, however, the half-wavelength increase in the distance to one of the stations is accompanied by a similar decrease in the distance to the other, making a total change of one wavelength in the distance-difference. Thus if in Fig.14 the transmitted frequency were 100 kHz, the lane-width on the baseline would be 1.5 km.

The LOPs are expressed in lanes and fractions although Decca readings also include a number and letter denoting groups of lanes (see Chapter 4). The respective frequencies used are such that 0.01 lane typically amounts to about 5 m for Decca and about 150 m for Omega. The baseline in Fig.14 has been made untypically short, whatever wavelength is assumed, in order to show a few lanes at a relatively large scale.

Ambiguity

Away from the centre-line AB of the pattern, the difference in the distances to the stations may be such that the phase difference between the two signals will amount to many whole cycles, plus the fractional value which the phasemeter measures. Accordingly the phasemeter (or, in modern receivers, its digital equivalent) includes an indicator which keeps count, like the hour hand of a clock, of the passage through successive lanes. Science offers no direct way of determining the whole number of cycles in the phase difference between two wave transmissions.

The position lines produced by the cw hyperbolic systems are ambiguous, because of this inability to distinguish one lane from another. Within a given lane, however, there is no ambiguity and on repeated visits to a given spot one may expect to obtain the same fractional reading each time, subject to the prevailing level of accuracy. A critic of systems of this kind in their early days said they 'tell you very accurately which pew you are sitting in, but not which church'.

Lane identification

In the absence of any other information from the receiver, the Decca or Omega user would have to know his starting position accurately enough to be sure of setting each of the lane-counting indicators to the correct lane. 'Accurately enough' means to better than plus/minus half a lane, at the user's position, in each of the two patterns used. When under way, an interruption in reception lasting longer than it took to cross half a lane might build in a permanent error of one or more lanes. To reduce problems such as these, which in principle tend to be more significant with Decca than with the much wider lanes of Omega, the stations of each system periodically transmit additional 'lane identification' signals as described in Chapters 4 and 6.

Effect of receiver motion

The question is sometimes asked whether corrections ought not in theory to be applied for the effect of the Doppler frequency-shifts on the received Omega or Decca signals, or on the Loran-C carrier wave, when the receiver is moving. The answer is that the hyperbolic systems do not, so to speak, work *in spite of* the Doppler effect: they demonstrate it. It has already been shown that when the receiver is moving towards a transmitter, for example, the phase of the received signal will advance because of the shortening signal path. A progressive advance in phase is tantamount to an upward shift in frequency, although perhaps by only a matter of cycles per hour: this is in fact the frequency-shift that constitutes the Doppler effect (see also Chapter 7).

Sorting out the signals

It was implied above that two cw stations generate a position line by transmitting continuously on the same frequency. Although from the user's point of view (and also as far as the lattice is concerned) the Decca and Omega systems behave exactly as if this were true, the receiver would in practice be unable to distinguish between two signals that were present together on the same frequency.

Accordingly, Omega signals are transmitted on the same frequency but not at the same time and the receiver memorises the phase of the absent one in order to derive the phase difference. In the case of Decca, a station pair transmits on frequencies that are different but are harmonically related (e.g. in the ratio 3:4) so that the receiver can multiply them to a common value. The phase difference is measured at the common frequency and it is to that frequency that the Decca lanes correspond.

Use of pulses

In the original version of Loran (Loran-A), hyperbolic position lines were created by comparing the arrival times of synchronised pulse signals in the way described in Chapters 1 and 2. The accuracy of the TD measurement depended on how clearly the receiver could identify, in

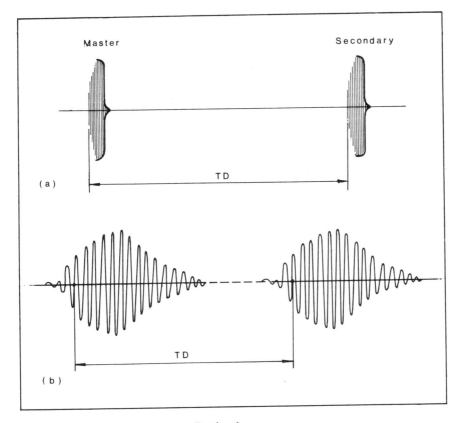

Fig. 15 Methods of measuring TD of pulses.
(a) TD between pulse envelopes (e.g. Loran-A). (b) TD between the same sampling point in phase-locked pulses (Loran-C).

terms of time, the leading edges of the two pulse 'envelopes'. In Fig. 15(a) the leading edges are blurred to illustrate this. One of the main improvements introduced by Loran-C was its use of a much more precise time datum than the leading edge.

Master and secondary (slave) Loran-C pulses are shown in detail in Fig.15(b). A pulse is a short transmission that lasts only a few cycles of the 'carrier' wave. For each of the signals, the datum point for measuring the TD will be seen to be the end of the third cycle. The use of specific cycles in this way means that the master and secondary carrier waves have to be phase-locked, like Decca and Omega signals, as part of the synchronising process. The fact that Loran-C takes account of individual cycles introduces the possibility of ambiguous position lines as described in Chapter 5.

Why the two techniques?

Although a similarity between the cw and pulse-type systems has just been noted, it may well be asked at this stage how two such basically different methods of producing hyperbolic position lines come to be in use. The main reason is that while Loran-C offers a superior combination of fix accuracy and coverage area to either Decca or Omega, the pulse signals it radiates have a tendency to cause, and to be vulnerable to, radio interference and this characteristic has restricted Loran deployment in some parts of the world. The sudden onset of a Loran pulse causes radiation on a wide band of frequencies around the carrier value, whereas an Omega or Decca signal occupies virtually a single or 'spot' frequency value since the only information such a signal has to convey is its own phase.

Groundwave and skywave

It is well known that the radio signals used by the hyperbolic systems travel to the receiver by two routes: directly along the earth's surface (the groundwave) and by way of a reflecting layer above the earth (the skywave). The computation of the lattice on charts and the corresponding software in processor-based receivers is based on the groundwave. In Fig.16 the ionosphere is drawn as a wavy line to show that as a reflector it behaves more like the endlessly moving waves of the sea than the smooth surface generally depicted in textbooks.

As a result of this motion, the phase of the skywave varies more or less randomly with respect to that of the groundwave. In the receiver the two components mix, presenting a resultant signal that varies in phase and strength as shown in the vector diagrams. In these the

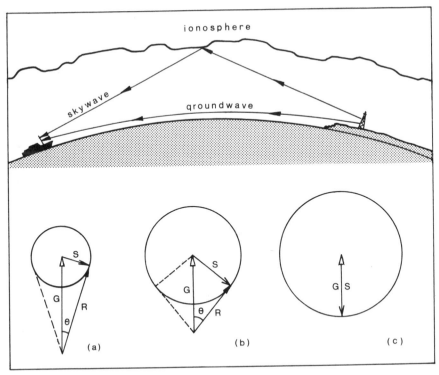

Fig. 16 Effect of skywave/groundwave interference.
   (a) Variations in ionosphere height cause phase of skywave S to vary
randomly (shown by circle) with respect to groundwave G. Resultant
signal R therefore varies in phase (θ) and strength (length of arrow). (b)
As range increases, G and S approach equality. R varies widely in phase
and strength. (c) If G = S they cancel out when in opposite phase and
signal is lost.

strength of the groundwave G and skywave S is represented by the
length of the respective arrows, and the phase by their direction. The
circle indicates the randomly-varying phase of the skywave with respect
to the groundwave. The resultant R represents the random variation
that this signal will contribute to the position line.

   Near the station the groundwave is much the stronger signal. As the
receiver-to-transmitter distance increases, groundwave signal strength
falls more rapidly than that of the skywave owing to absorption of
energy by the terrain or water along the path. When it falls to equality
with the skywave, as in Fig.16(c), there will be occasional signal loss
(through cancellation of skywave and groundwave) as well as large
resultant phase variations. This is the factor that sets the limit to the
coverage of a given chain of Decca stations. Interference between the
different modes of propagation also conditions the performance and

coverage of the Omega system, albeit in a complex fashion since the signals propagate within what amounts to a waveguide formed by the earth and the ionosphere.

In the case of Loran, however, the transmissions consist of short pulses repeated at relatively long intervals and this enables advantage to be taken of the delay in the arrival of the skywave pulse due to its longer journey. Generally the delay is such that the skywave signal does not start to arrive until after the third cycle of the groundwave signal has been received, thus allowing the receiver to extract the time information without contamination by the skywave (see Chapter 5, Fig.27). This ability to eliminate the unwanted skywave component of the signals, except at very long ranges, gives a Loran-C chain a relatively large coverage area compared with Decca.

Monitor stations

Elaborate techniques are used at the transmitting stations of a hyperbolic chain to ensure that the radiated signals remain stable and correctly synchronised. Obviously, however, it is essential to keep the service under continuous external observation and accordingly each of the three systems has a network of receiving stations established at precisely-known locations where the patterns and the individual signals are monitored. As well as detecting and reporting any transmission anomaly as soon as it occurs, the monitor stations acquire a vast volume of practical data on signal propagation from their continuous observations and this helps to improve and refine the predictions of system performance.

Effects of weather

The performance of the on-board receiver for any of the hyperbolic systems can be reduced or nullified by icing on the antenna and by the effects of local precipitation static interference in snow and rain. Special care should be taken when using the receiver under such conditions.

The on-board installation

Position fixing receivers, especially those for the hyperbolic systems, often have to deal with weak signals that are highly vulnerable to electrical interference. On any type or size of craft the installation and wiring of the antenna and its feeder, and of the receiver unit and any associated equipment, call for close attention to detail. The manufacturer's instructions, particularly in regard to antenna siting and earth (ground) wiring, should be rigidly adhered to, regardless of whether some different arrangement might be thought to look neater or to save cable.

Summary

The frequency, wavelength and propagation speed of a radio signal bear a simple relationship. The difference in the arrival time of continuous wave (cw) signals is found by comparing their phase and is displayed in lanes and lane fractions. The lane-width is minimum, and constant, on the baseline. Lane ambiguity is resolved by a counting process and/or by additional transmissions (lane identification). Interference by the skywave component of the signal affects the cw systems but can be largely eliminated in a pulse system. The rotation of signal phase in a moving receiver demonstrates the Doppler effect. Be sure to follow the receiver manufacturer's instructions in wiring the shipboard installation.

4

The Decca Navigator

Origin and status

The basic principles of the continuous wave hyperbolic system that
became the Decca Navigator were conceived in 1937 in the United
States. After initial experiments there, and further development in the
UK by the Decca Company in collaboration with the (then) Admiralty
Signal Establishment, the system was first used in 1944 for the
navigation of minesweepers and landing craft in the Normandy
invasion. From November 1945 it became available commercially and in
the following year the first chain of stations started transmitting,
covering the Thames estuary and its approaches. As the maritime
community gained experience of the system, requirements for extension
of the coverage grew and there are now (1986) 43 Decca chains in
operation.

The coverage includes the coastal waters of NW Europe and of parts
of Africa, the Persian Gulf, India, Australia, and Japan. Many thousands
of vessels use the system, including large numbers of fishing craft for
which it is the principal navigational aid in many areas. It is also used by
aircraft and particularly by helicopters employed for oil rig communica-
tion and air/sea rescue. Under the best conditions Decca has the highest
accuracy of the three hyperbolic navigational aids, although its
maximum range is the shortest.

Decca chains

Decca stations are grouped in 'chains' of four or, in a few cases, three.
The chains vary widely in layout with baselines between about 70 km
and 170 km in length. Range is typically in the order of 440 km (240
n.mile) from the master station by night, and about twice that distance
by day; accuracy is as high as a few tens of metres in the best part of the
coverage in summer daytime, falling to several km at night near the limit
of range. Information is published on the accuracy and coverage of
every Decca chain, in a form which takes account of diurnal and
seasonal variations, as described later.

The stations disposed around the master are known as slaves
because their transmissions are locked in a precise phase relationship

with the master signal. In parts of the world where bad reception conditions are liable to affect the phase-locking, atomic-reference oscillators are used as the source of the transmitted signals. Every station has comprehensive automatically-switched changeover facilities which preserve continuity of transmission in the event of a fault in the equipment or power supply. The transmissions have a high reputation for reliability, and an outage-time of zero seconds in a year of 24-hour operation is not unknown for a Decca station.

Frequencies

The different chains are distinguished one from the other by transmitting on slightly different frequencies, although there are one or two cases where chains are far enough apart (thousands of miles) to employ the same frequencies without risk of interference. Selecting the chain to be used involves tuning the on-board receiver to the correct set of four frequencies, which can be done simply by keying-in a code comprising a number from 0 to 10 and a letter from A to E. Some receivers automatically select the correct chain on the basis of stored data, given an estimate of the present position, and confirm the chain selected by displaying the code. Some receivers use a special code.

The transmissions fall in four small frequency bands between 70 and 130 kHz. Sample frequency values are shown in Table 1, where the slave stations are identified by the colour in which the respective pattern is depicted on lattice charts.

The frequencies transmitted by a chain are multiples of a value f between 14.0 and 14.4 kHz, but no signal in that band is actually radiated. The transmitted frequencies are so related that the receiver can

Table 1   Transmitted and comparison frequencies: Decca chain 05B

Transmitted frequencies		
Station	*Frequency (kHz)*	*Harmonic*
Master	85.0000	6f
Purple slave	70.8333	5f
Red slave	113.3333	8f
Green slave	127.5000	9f

Phase comparison frequencies and lane/zone widths			
Pattern	*Frequency (kHz)*	*Harmonic*	*Width on baseline*
Purple lanes	425	30f	352.1 m
Red lanes	340	24f	440.1 m
Green lanes	255	18f	586.8 m
Zones (all patterns)	14.1666	1f	10562.0 m

multiply them to common values for phase comparison. For example it multiplies the master (6f) frequency by 2 and the green slave frequency by 3 to produce a common value of 18f, and the green pattern is exactly what would result if it were possible for both stations to radiate an 18f signal. This 'trick' of using frequency multiplication to simulate the transmission of signals of the same frequency from a pair of stations was one of the key features of the original invention.

Zones and lanes

The plotting of a fix from two Decca LOPs is illustrated in Fig.17, where the receiver is in red/green coverage. The third (purple) pattern and slave are therefore omitted. The lattice is of course simplified in this

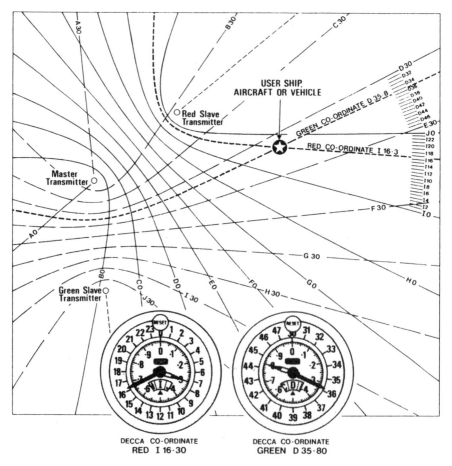

Fig. 17 Plotting a fix from old-style Decometers.

drawing where the scale is too small to show the lanes except near the right-hand edge. The hyperbolas shown are the boundaries of the 'zones' into which lanes are grouped. Zones are identified by the letters A–J, starting from the master and repeating the sequence once or more depending on the length of the baseline.

When the baseline contains more than one group of zones A–J, the groups are numbered 1, 2, etc., to avoid uncertainty when entering such readings into a processor. The Data Sheets mentioned at the end of this chapter include maps showing the zone groups for every chain.

The red lanes (24 per zone) are numbered 0–23, the green (18 per zone) 30–47 and the purple (30 per zone) 50–79: this avoids the need to specify the colour when reporting a position. The lanes of the three patterns are of different width owing to the different phase-comparison frequencies, but on the baselines the zones of all three patterns have the same width of about 10 km (see Table 1).

Normally the lane numbering starts at the respective master baseline extension, with 1A 00.00 for the red pattern, 1A 30.00 (green) and 1A 50.00 (purple). In a few cases this convention is departed from, generally not by a large fraction of a lane, when the operating authority has found an excessive level of fixed error in some important part of the coverage: by adjusting the phasing of the slave station with respect to the master, the level of error in the area concerned can be reduced and this results in a corresponding deviation from zero on the master baseline extension.

Ambiguity

In Fig. 17 the LOPs are displayed on a pair of old-style Decometers which illustrate the basis of the LOP better than a digital readout. The lane fraction in hundredths is unambiguous. As explained in the previous chapter, the lane numbers (Red 16, Green 35) and the zone letters (I and D) are derived by what amounts to a count of the revolutions made by the fraction pointer shaft, or a computer equivalent of that process, as the ship crosses the successive lanes.

In principle the counting process requires the user to set the zone and lane indicators to the correct values at his starting position. To do this when the ship is on or near a baseline, where the lanes are only a few hundred metres wide, the position would have to be known beforehand with an accuracy (better than plus/minus half a lane in each pattern) that would seldom be attainable in practice especially in darkness or when out of sight of shore marks.

Accordingly, every chain radiates periodic 'lane identification' signals which positively indicate the correct lane numbers given that the zones are known. This leaves the ambiguity represented by the zones, which initially the receiver cannot distinguish between, but the ambiguous position lines are nowhere less than 10 km apart and are several times more widely spaced in the outer parts of the coverage. In general mariners have not found the zone ambiguity a serious problem.

Lane identification

The lower the frequency of the signals that are phase-compared to create a hyperbolic pattern, the wider the resulting lanes since these depend on the wavelength. If therefore the master and, say, the red slave stations were periodically to radiate additional signals from which the receiver could extract the very low frequency f (defined above) for phase comparison, this would have the effect of superimposing on the red lanes a coarse pattern of lanes 24 times wider. The on-board receiver would have an additional phasemeter working at frequency f and calibrated in the red lane numbers 0–23; each time the coarse pattern came into being the pointer would indicate which lane the ship was in, within the known zone. This is the essence of the lane identification (LI) facility that a Decca chain provides for all three patterns every 20 seconds.

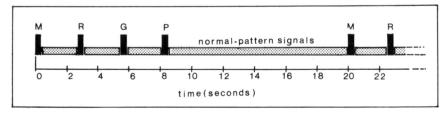

Fig. 18 Lane identification timing sequence (approximate).

The four stations of a chain send LI signals in the sequence shown in Fig.18. Each signal lasts less than 0.5 s, during which time all other signals from the chain are turned off: the interruption of the otherwise continuous normal-pattern transmission is too short to affect the on-board receiver. No new frequencies are involved and each LI transmission consists of the four frequencies allocated to the chain – 5f, 6f, 8f, 9f – radiated together from the station concerned in a fixed phase relationship. A trigger signal (omitted with other details from the diagram) from the master station precedes each LI transmission and switches the chain and receivers to the LI mode for the half-second.

The four-fold transmissions are known as multipulse (MP) signals and from each the receiver extracts a frequency f with which to generate the coarse pattern as described above. The stations do not transmit their respective MP signals simultaneously and the receiver therefore has to memorise the phase of the f-frequency signal obtained from the master and compare it with that from each slave in order to derive the LI readings. An essential property of the composite MP signals, since they are depended upon to resolve the lane ambiguity, is their greater reliability under skywave interference compared with the individual signals that generate the fine patterns.

On receivers that display LI readings (some use the signals without displaying the readings) these appear in the order master–red–green–purple. The master reading should normally be zero since it results in effect from comparing the memorised phase of previous signals with that of the signal being received; a zero master LI reading thus forms a confidence-check on the LI process. A value other than zero (plus or minus a small tolerance) indicates an error which the user resolves by some simple action depending on the receiver type. The three LI readings follow at a rate allowing comfortable observation and comparison with the lane-number display, which the user (or the processor) will reset if several successive LI readings show it to be in error.

LI discrepancy

The desired frequency f is extracted from the MP signal in different ways depending on the type of receiver, and the manner of using the LI information varies similarly. In some equipment the LI readout is supplemented by an alarm which functions when the processor detects a discrepancy between the lane number arrived at by the counting process and the lane number indicated by LI. The alarm is thus a warning that the displayed lat/long position or waypoint data may be in error by a distance equivalent to one or more whole lanes. Once the discrepancy can be accounted for the user keys in a command to update the erroneous lane number.

Position from LI readings

Because an MP transmission is a four-fold source of data (in radio parlance it has four-fold frequency diversity) the phase of the f-frequency signal obtained from it is more stable in the presence of skywave interference than are its individual components. For this reason the LI readings are often used, especially at night and/or at long ranges, to provide the LOPs for the position fix in preference to the so-called normal patterns. In some regions where skywave interference tends to be high, especially near the magnetic Equator where the ionosphere is a more efficient reflector than elsewhere, this mode of position fixing is recommended officially at night-time.

In principle the accuracy of an LOP obtained from the LI signals will be lower than that of the normal lane and fraction display, e.g. by a nominal factor of 24 in the case of the red LOP, but especially in bad conditions the high stability of the MP signals tends to compensate for this. In some receivers the LI readings are processed so as to achieve a nominal resolution of 0.01 lane and these are referred to as LIP (lane identification pattern) readings. LIP is sometimes interpreted as 'LI precision' because of the 0.01 lane resolution.

At any given location, fixed error values tend to be different for the LI patterns and the normal patterns. It is to the normal patterns that published fixed error corrections refer.

Receiver variants

Decca receivers of the period before the microprocessor are exemplified by the Mark 21 which was introduced in the early 1970s but remains in use in large numbers. It provides LOP readings on Decometer indicators for manual plotting on a lattice chart, together with a digital LI readout, but has no built-in co-ordinate conversion or waypoint facilities. The Mark 21 is however often used to drive an electromechanical or video plotter.

An example of a modern receiver is the Decca Yacht Navigator III. To minimise size and power drain, this receiver uses only the 6f and 8f signals that are radiated as part of the MP transmissions. Position is displayed in lat/long and waypoint form rather than in LOPs and the position fix is based on lanes having the width that would result from comparing phase at $8f - 6f = 2f$. This avoids the high ambiguity of the normal lane patterns and leaves ambiguous LOPs separated by some 5 km as a minimum.

Current Decca receivers include multi-sensor equipment capable of processing Decca, Loran-C, Omega and Transit signals and embodying, in one form or another, the features and facilities outlined in Chapters 8 and 9.

Range and coverage

The different chains vary to some extent in maximum range but typically this is about 250 n.mile (460 km) by night and about 400 n.mile (640 km) by day. The name of each chain in operation is shown in Table 2, together with the identifying number and letter in the frequency code. Not all makes or types of Decca receiver are necessarily equipped to receive every chain.

Table 2 Decca chains and frequency codes (1986)

European chains	*Chains outside Europe*
0A South Baltic (Sweden)	1C South Persian Gulf
0E Vestlandet (Norway)	2C East Newfoundland
1B South West British	2C Hokuriko (Japan)
2A Northumbrian	2F Salaya (India West)
2E Holland	4A Namaqua (S. Africa)
3B North British	4C Shikoku (Japan)
3E Lofoten (Norway)	6A Cape (S. Africa)
3F German	6C Bangladesh
4B North Baltic	6C Tohoku (Japan)
4C North West Spanish	7B Bombay (India West)
4E Trondelag (Norway)	7C Kyushu (Japan)
5B English	8A Eastern Province (S. Africa)
5F North Bothnian	8B Calcutta (India East)
6A South Spanish	8C Kanto (Japan)
6C North Scottish	8E Dampier (Australia)
6E Gulf of Finland	9C S.W. Africa
7B Danish	9C Hokkaido (Japan)
7D Irish	10C Natal (S. Africa)
7E Finnmark (Norway)	
8B French	
8C South Bothnian	
8E Hebridean	
9B Frisian Islands	
9E Helgeland (Norway)	
10B Skagerrak	

Fixed errors

Correction data based on fixed errors measured in many different areas are published in map form (Fig.19). If no corrections are published for a given area, it should not be assumed that there is no distortion of the patterns in that area. Errors in a lattice chart, e.g. in registration or in coastline positions, are not of course eliminated when corrections are applied for fixed errors in the LOPs.

Variable errors

Estimated variable errors for each Decca chain are published in the form of contour diagrams. There are separate diagrams for full daylight (Fig.20), when variable errors are least, and for other times (Fig.21). In the latter case the contours are interpreted in conjunction with a so-called 'onion' diagram and an associated table (Fig.22). Calculation of the error values is based on the Drms criterion described in Chapter 2.

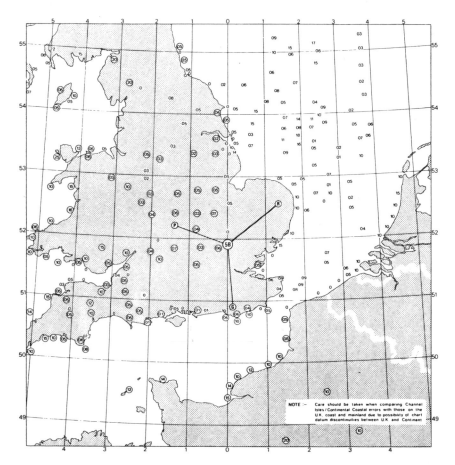

Fig. 19 Fixed error correction chart.
Showing corrections (hundredths of a lane) to be applied to observed
Red normal-pattern readings, chain 5B. Subtract circled figures, add
figures not circled.

The error margins indicated in the Data Sheets are good working figures
but should not be taken as maximum values: statistically there is a
1-in-20 chance that the actual error will exceed twice the value given in
the table. The figures in the table take no account of fixed errors and
assume that appropriate corrections for these have been applied.

The change in the level of error from daylight to night is gradual. At
dawn and dusk the errors will be rather greater than in full daylight.
Extreme night errors are unlikely to occur until the sun is well below
the horizon. Conditions change from day to day. In general, variable
errors are worst in winter night-time. When large variable errors are
suspected it will always help to plot the position frequently, if possible

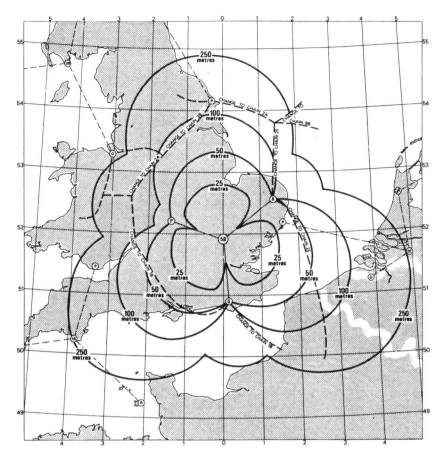

Fig. 20 Accuracy contours for full daylight.
Contours enclose areas (chain 5B) in which it is predicted that fix repeatability errors will not exceed the distances shown on 68% of occasions during FULL DAYLIGHT as defined in Fig. 22.

comparing it with the position found by dead reckoning or other independent sources.

Two-chain fixing

Improved accuracy, resulting from a better angle of cut, can be obtained in certain areas by forming the position-fix from the intersection of an LOP from one chain with an LOP from a neighbouring chain. Special inter-chain charts are available for those areas, which in general are near the fringe of the coverage.

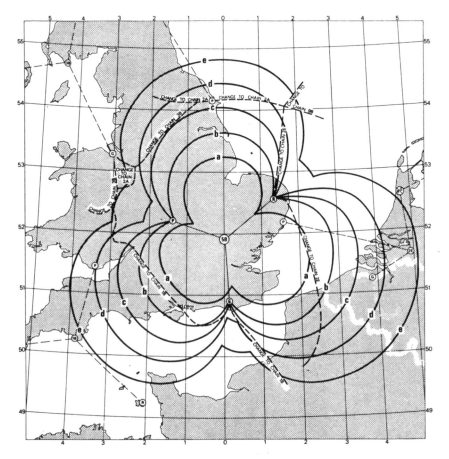

Fig. 21 Accuracy contours for times other than full daylight.
Predicted coverage and accuracy (chain 5B) based on 68% probability
level, for times defined in Fig. 22.

Warning notices

Pre-planned outages or changes in the Decca transmissions, e.g.
through temporary use of a reserve antenna system, are announced in
the weekly editions of *Notices to Mariners* (obtainable from official Chart
Agents) as are details of amendments to charts. Reports of unforeseen
outages or disturbance of the signals are broadcast as Decca Warnings
by coastal R/T or W/T stations in the vicinity (listed in the Data Sheets
referred to below) and by the NAVTEX system where it is in operation.
NAVTEX is a radio telex service carrying navigation-related data on a
common frequency channel (518.0 kHz) allocated for world-wide use.

RANDOM FIXING ERRORS AT SEA LEVEL IN NAUTICAL MILES
68% PROBABILITY LEVEL

DECCA PERIOD	CONTOUR				
See Time and Season Factor Diagram below	a	b	c	d	e
HALF LIGHT	⟨0·10	⟨0·10	⟨0·10	0·13	0·25
DAWN/DUSK	⟨0·10	⟨0·10	0·13	0·25	0·50
SUMMER NIGHT	⟨0·10	0·13	0·25	0·50	1·00
WINTER NIGHT	0·10	0·18	0·37	0·75	1·50

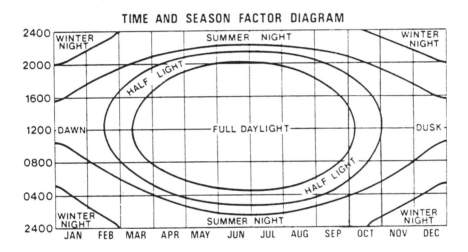

TIME AND SEASON FACTOR DIAGRAM

Fig. 22 Table and onion diagram used with Fig. 21.
Table gives predicted variable fixing errors not likely to be exceeded in more than one out of three readings.

Lattice charts

Marine charts overprinted with the Decca LOPs are produced and issued by government navigational and hydrographic authorities of many nations. Lattice charts and plotting sheets are also published by fishing cartographers and agencies including Racal-Decca. All charts are normally sold to users by Chart Agents and stockists.

Admiralty Decca charts carry references to the colour overlays in which the red, green and purple patterns are denoted by the letters AB, AC and AD respectively: A represents the master and B, C, D the slaves.

Publications on Decca

Detailed data on the coverage and predicted accuracy of each chain are given in the Decca Navigator Marine Data Sheets published by Racal-Decca Navigator Limited, 247 Burlington Road, New Malden, Surrey KT3 4NF, UK. A Racal-Decca publication (*Decca Navigator: Principles and Performance of the System*) gives a technical description of the system with particular reference to the factors governing accuracy and coverage. The *Admiralty List of Radio Signals* Vol. V (HMSO) includes chapters on Decca, Loran, Omega and Satellite Navigation.

5

Loran-C

Origin and status

The original Loran system, which became known as Loran-A, was invented in the USA in 1940 and developed by the Radiation Laboratory of the Massachusetts Institute of Technology. By the end of the Second World War some 70 Loran stations covered a large part of the world and served about 75000 ships and aircraft. After the war an improved version, Loran-C, was developed and the first such chain became operational in 1957. By 1981 Loran-C had replaced the A version throughout North America and Europe, although a few Loran-A chains are still deployed (none by the United States Coast Guard) in the Far East.

Today the Loran-C chains operated by the USCG cover large areas of the northern hemisphere as well as the Coastal Confluence Zone of the USA. The system is extensively used by ships of all types for coastal and ocean navigation, and also by aircraft and on land. In general Loran-C offers a superior combination of accuracy and coverage area to that of any system yet devised for fixing position by reference to earth-based transmitting stations.

Chain configuration

A Loran-C chain consists of a master station and from two to four outlying secondary stations, radiating synchronised pulse transmissions. Synchronism is achieved by equipping each of the stations with high-stability atomic-reference oscillators as the signal sources. The baselines vary widely, being relatively short where they lie over land, with an average length of about 1000 km (540 n.mile). For this reason the maximum range available varies considerably from chain to chain, but generally the groundwave coverage extends at least 600 n.mile (1111 km) offshore from a coastal master station.

LOP patterns

The secondary stations, and the respective hyperbolic patterns they generate in conjunction with the master, are identified by the letters W,

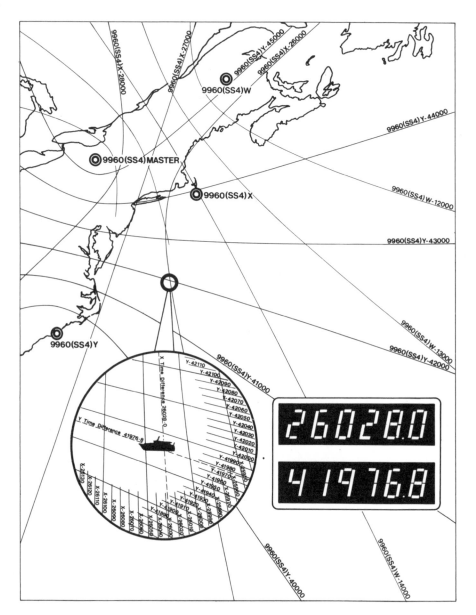

Fig. 23 Plotting a Loran-C fix.

X, Y and Z. When more than two patterns are available the user (or the processor in the case of an automatic receiver) chooses the two that give the best angle of cut. The plotting of a position on a lattice chart is illustrated in Fig.23, where the X and Y patterns are used for the fix. In addition to an LOP display, modern Loran receivers provide a latitude/longitude readout, waypoint facilities and other refinements (see Chapters 8 and 9).

Loran-C receivers generally give a continuous display of the TD readings relating to one of the patterns, as selected, or two. The TD is normally a six-digit number in microseconds and tenths and the LOPs printed on the lattice charts are numbered to correspond. The first two digits of the TD identify the pattern independently of the letters W, X, etc., being a function of the 'coding delay' which is unique for each pattern, as described later.

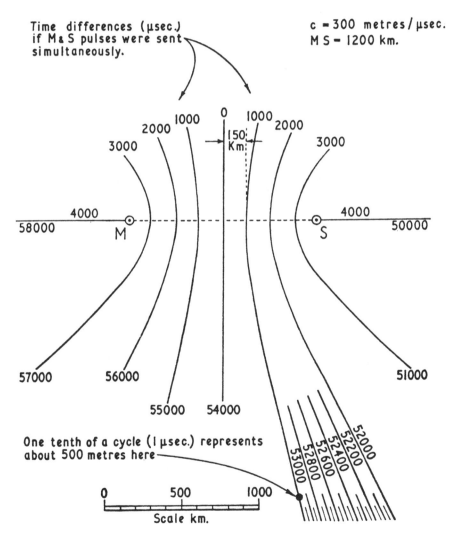

Fig. 24 Principle of Loran-C pattern numbering.

TD numbering

In Fig.24, M and S represent master and secondary stations on a baseline 1200 km in length. Above the baseline MS, the TD numbering corresponds with the description in Chapter 1 of an elementary hyperbolic system in which it was assumed for simplicity that the master and secondary pulses are radiated simultaneously. For the 1200 km baseline and a propagation speed of 300 m/μs the TD values would be as shown, with 4000 μs on the two baseline extensions.

In practice, the pulses are not sent together since this would result, near the central '0' line, in TD values too small to deal with. Also the receiver would not know which pulse was the first to arrive, making the TDs ambiguous. It is therefore arranged that the master always transmits first; the secondaries follow in a sequence, each with a fixed (coding) delay which is made long enough to ensure that nowhere in the coverage would a secondary signal arrive before the master.

The illustration shows the effect of a 50000-μs coding delay. The delay is the time interval between the arrival of the master signal at the secondary station and the emission of the secondary pulse, and results in a TD value of 50000 μs on the secondary baseline extension. The secondary signal takes 4000 μs to travel the length of the baseline to the master, resulting in a TD value of 58000 μs on the master baseline extension (remembering that the master signal will have taken 4000 μs to get to the secondary station).

Group repetition interval (GRI)

Loran-C stations all transmit on the same frequency, that is to say they all transmit pulses consisting of short bursts of a 100 kHz radio wave. The repeated sequence in which the master and secondary stations transmit is known as a *group* and recurs at a fixed group repetition interval (GRI). The GRI is different for each chain and therefore identifies the chain. It is normally expressed in tens of microseconds as a four-digit number, thus a GRI of 9990 indicates a repetition rate of just over 10 groups per second. In the past a letter/number code was used, shown in the list in Table 3.

Accuracy and coverage data

Data on the accuracy and coverage of Loran-C are presented in publications issued by the United States Coast Guard (e.g. *Loran-C User Handbook*, ref. COMDTINST M 16562.3 of May 1980 and later editions) and by the United States Defense Mapping Agency (DMA).

Table 3   Loran-C chains in operation (1986)

Name	GRI	Old code
Mediterranean Sea	7990	SL1
Norwegian Sea	7970	SL3
Icelandic	9980	SS2
Labrador Sea	7930	SL7
Canadian East Coast	5930	SH7
North-east US	9960	SS4
South-east US	7980	SL2
Great Lakes	8970	—
US West Coast	9940	SS6
Canadian West Coast	5990	SH1
Gulf of Alaska	7960	SL4
Central Pacific	4990	S1
North Pacific	9990	SS1
North-west Pacific	9970	SS3
Saudi Arabia North	8990	—
Saudi Arabia South	7170	—

ASF errors

Errors that remain fixed with time are known in the context of Loran-C by the term ASF (additional secondary phase factor). ASF errors vary in magnitude and are especially significant in coastal localities to which one or more of the signals travel over land. Away from land, ASF values tend to change more gradually from place to place than in coastal areas. ASF correction tables are published for chains located in the continental US, for use in conjunction with lattice charts that do not incorporate ASF corrections. Some charts carry lattices that have been adjusted to take account of predicted or observed ASF data (this will be stated on the chart) and the tables should therefore not be used when plotting fixes on such charts.

Variable errors

As explained in Chapter 3, Loran's use of pulse transmissions enables the on-board receiver to reject the unwanted skywave component of the signal which arrives by reflection from the ionosphere. This ability holds good up to distances of several hundred miles from the stations and the area within which it operates is known as the 'groundwave coverage' of a given chain (see Fig.25 for an example).

   The level of variable error is low throughout the groundwave coverage, for example USCG diagrams indicate for good signal/noise conditions a Standard Deviation of 0.1 µs. The corresponding variation

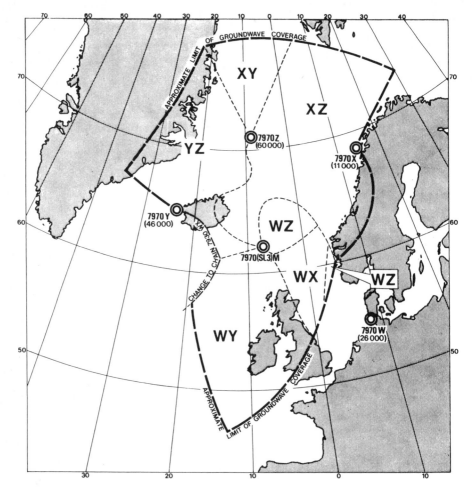

Fig. 25 Estimated groundwave coverage of a Loran-C chain (7970).

in terms of distance depends of course on the local expansion factor (gradient) and angle of cut (crossing angle); throughout a large part of the groundwave coverage area the fix accuracy is rated at 1500 feet using the conservative 2 Drms criterion (95% probability level).

As range from the stations increases there comes a point, especially at night, at which the groundwave signal strength falls to a level approaching equality with the skywave and the receiver can then no longer discriminate between the two components. Indications that this may be happening are an unusually high signal strength, wide fluctuations in signal strength and/or TD, and consequently large variations in the apparent position. The skywave can however be used, with a resulting extension of the range available but with much reduced accuracy, as described later.

Interference rejection

Radio transmissions from other services using frequencies falling within or near the band allotted to Loran-C (90–110 kHz) can interfere with Loran reception. The result may be a varying TD or even failure by the receiver to acquire the chain signals, unless steps are taken to tune-out the interference. This is achieved by a notch filter, so called because it makes a notch or trough in the receiver's response to the radio spectrum at the unwanted frequency. Notch filters are of various types, some are set manually and others automatically search for and reject strong interfering transmission(s).

The strongest interfering signal is not necessarily the most harmful. A relatively weak signal that is 'synchronous' (i.e. its frequency happens to bear some simple and stable numerical relationship to the Loran-C carrier) can adversely affect Loran performance. For this reason users are officially recommended to consult the receiver manufacturer as to the proper notching procedure if they have difficulties with signal acquisition or tracking in areas where such interference is present.

The USCG *Loran-C User Handbook* mentioned earlier emphasises the importance of following the notching procedure given in the operating instructions for the receiver in use. The same handbook also mentions a subsidiary function of the type of notch filter that includes a signal strength meter: if interference from other electrical equipment on board is suspected, this will be confirmed if the meter reading remains high at all settings of the notch filter tuning control (such interference normally occupies the full frequency band covered by the filter).

Cycle ambiguity

Under adverse conditions, for example if the receiver is attempting to acquire the signals at a long distance from the stations and/or in a high level of electrical noise, the problem of ambiguous position lines can present itself. To explain this it is necessary to look at how the receiver measures the TD between the arrival of the master and a secondary signal.

In Fig.26 the master and part of a secondary pulse are shown and individual cycles of the respective 100 kHz carrier waves can be seen. To measure the TD the receiver creates synthetic 'gate' pulses, holds these in time coincidence with the incoming pulses, and measures the TD between the gate pulses as shown. The gate pulses are strong and noise-free, which helps to make the measurement accurate, and are lined up with the respective incoming signals by an automatic process known as tracking.

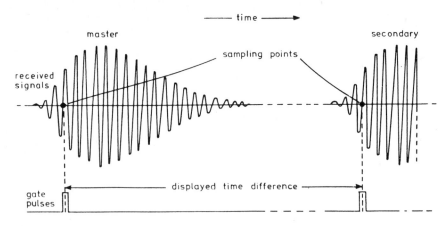

Fig. 26 Use of gate pulses to measure TD.

The gate pulse tracks a specific point in the corresponding incoming pulse and this 'sampling' point is normally the end of the third cycle. Since one cycle of a 100 kHz signal lasts 10 µs, the sampling point occurs 30 µs after the start of the pulse. Herein lies the secret of Loran-C's ability to reject the skywave-borne pulse which, because of its relatively long journey via the ionosphere, seldom if ever arrives sooner than 35 µs after the groundwave. As shown in Fig.27, the TD measurement is thus free from skywave contamination, provided of course that the master and secondary pulses are each tracked at the third cycle.

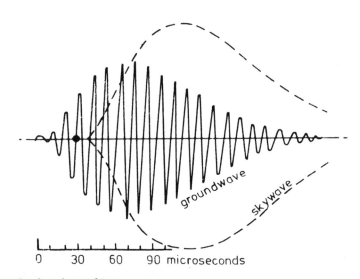

Fig. 27 Third-cycle tracking.
The 30 µs sampling point is free from contamination by the delayed skywave which arrives 35 µs (or later) after groundwave.

The ambiguity lies in the fact that if for some reason the tracking of one of the incoming pulses should jump to a different cycle, this would cause a TD error of 10 μs or a multiple of 10 μs. Thus if the receiver were to track the fourth cycle of the master pulse and the third cycle of the secondary, the measured TD would be in error by −10 μs. The resulting error in the LOP would amount to 1.5 km on the baseline and would be greater elsewhere due to the pattern expansion.

To summarise, the user should be aware that in adverse conditions a large error in the LOP corresponding to 10 μs or a multiple thereof can suddenly present itself. Most Loran-C receivers will generally, though not invariably, give a warning signal when such a change occurs.

Integrate/track mode

Once third-cycle tracking has been achieved, Loran-C receivers generally adopt, either automatically or at the user's discretion, the 'integrate' or 'track' mode of operation. This disables the circuitry concerned with identifying and selecting the third cycle, so lessening the possibility of cycle-jumps, and relies on the integrity of the tracking process which can be very high given suitable filtering techniques. This is in general the normal mode in which the receiver is used.

When navigating near the limit of the groundwave coverage of a given chain, or perhaps under bad reception conditions, some receivers allow the user to make the sampling point 'move up into the pulse', as the jargon puts it, and track a stronger cycle than the third (e.g. the

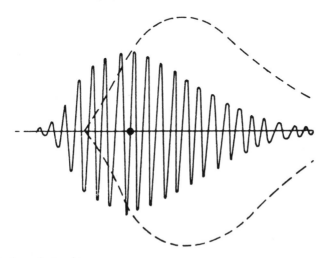

Fig. 28 Peak cycle tracking.
    Tracking the 7th cycle improves signal/noise performance but loses the immunity to skywave.

seventh) of the master and the secondary pulse. This considerably extends the distance from the stations at which the receiver can be used, but at the cost of reduced accuracy through losing the immunity to skywave interference (Fig.28). At very long ranges, and more especially at night, the skywave will tend to become the predominant component of the signal.

Skywave operation

The feasibility of operating when the skywave is predominant varies with the type of receiver, some of which are intended primarily for use within the groundwave coverage area, and generally calls for skill and experience on the part of the user. Some charts carry skywave correction data for the cases where one or both the signals of a pair are skywaves (known as sky/ground and sky/sky corrections) to be applied when plotting the LOPs on the chart.

A USCG publication gives the following example of skywave correction data: 7980Y −04N GS+54N, where 7980 is the chain rate and Y the LOP pattern concerned. −04 means subtract 4 μs from the TD reading if the master and secondary signals are both skywaves. N means that the correction is to be applied at night only (D for day). GS+54N means that 54 μs must be added to the TD reading before plotting the fix if the receiver is tracking a groundwave master and a skywave secondary signal at night. SG would indicate a skywave master and groundwave secondary signal.

Envelope to cycle difference (ECD)

Returning once again to the automatic selection of the third cycle, the receiver depends for this upon the rigorously standardised shape (envelope) to which all transmitted Loran-C pulses conform. In particular it relies upon the precise rate or slope at which the early part of the pulse rises in strength from zero to peak. The envelope follows a mathematical law which in principle allows appropriate logic techniques to distinguish the third cycle from those before and after it.

In practice the envelope of the received pulse can become distorted in shape, for example through a complex effect that occurs when the signal has travelled along a path that is very long and/or passes over land of low electrical conductivity. In some localities the distortion can reach a level such that the receiver tends to select the wrong cycle, introducing the ambiguity mentioned earlier. The degree of pulse distortion can be expressed in time units and an undistorted pulse is said to have an ECD (envelope to cycle difference) of 0 μs.

Proper receiver design can provide some tolerance of pulse distortion and an ECD up to at least 3.5 µs can generally be accepted without the cycle-selection breaking down. Propagation conditions that give rise to an ECD tend not to change with time and it is therefore possible to apply a correction for ECD from the receiver keyboard in a locality where the value has been determined by observation and made known to users. Some receivers automatically apply corrections for ECD as a function of range from the stations.

Blink signal

At the Loran-C transmitting stations stringent precautions are taken against interruption or malfunctioning of the emitted signals. If, however, a transmission should be significantly disturbed the chain will transmit a 'blink' signal. Receivers recognise this signal and display a corresponding alarm (for details refer to the *User's Manual*).

Warning notices

Notification of planned changes in the Loran-C transmissions and charts, and reports of signal outages, are issued through *Notices to Mariners* and similar channels to those for Decca (see Chapter 4).

Lattice charts

Loran-C lattice charts for marine use are available from authorised Chart Agents. Such charts are produced by US Government agencies including the National Ocean Survey and the Hydrographic and Topographic Center of the Defense Mapping Agency.

Publications on Loran-C

The *Loran-C User Handbook* mentioned earlier is obtainable from the US Government Printing Office, Washington DC 20402. Coverage diagrams and data sheets relating to USCG-controlled Loran-C chains are included in *Coast Guard Navigation Systems Books*, Part 2, issued by Commandant (G-NRN-3), USCG Headquarters, 2100 Second Street SW, Washington DC 20593. ASF Correction Tables for Loran-C chains covering the US Coastal Confluence Zone are issued by the Defense Mapping Agency, Office of Distribution Services (Attention: DDCP), Washington DC 20315.

6
Omega

Origin and status

The Omega vlf (very low frequency) position fixing system was the outcome of extensive investigations into vlf propagation carried out in the USA from about 1950. The work included full-scale trials with an experimental system known as Radux. Omega in its present form first emerged in the 1960s and deployment of the station network was finally completed in August 1982. Operation of the station network is the responsibility of the Omega Navigation System Operations Detail (ONSOD) under the technical control of the Office of Navigation, United States Coast Guard.

The proportions and performance of Omega are those of an aid to oceanic marine and air navigation. As such it is probably not of interest to more than a minority of yachtsmen, particularly in the northern hemisphere where Loran and Decca coverage is concentrated. Omega is not widely used as an independent or stand-alone aid to navigation, but an on-board processor can exploit the complementary features of Omega and the Transit system so as to produce a global navigational aid with an overall performance markedly superior to that of either sensor individually.

Position line patterns

The Omega system consists of eight stations which in principle combine to cover the whole surface of the earth. Patterns of LOPs are overprinted on charts and maps (Fig.29) and may also be constructed from published tables. The stations are identified by the letters A–H (see list below), and the letters of a station pair identify the pattern they generate. Thus the stations in Norway and Liberia generate the AB pattern. The patterns consist of lanes, defined in Chapter 3. Lane numbering runs from the lower letter to the higher, e.g. from station G to station H in the GH pattern. In all cases the central lane boundary, coincident with the great circle bisecting the baseline, is numbered 900. To avoid obscuring other details, charts normally show only every third lane.

The stations transmit on several different frequencies in a sequence which is repeated every 10 s. Phase comparison at one of these

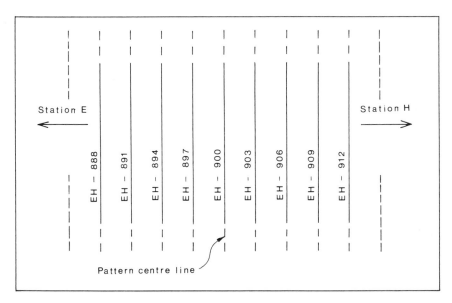

Fig. 29 Omega LOP numbering.

frequencies, 10.2 kHz, is the basis of the lane patterns printed on marine charts, resulting in a lane-width on the baselines of about 15 km. Receiver resolution is normally to 0.01 lane or 1 centilane, equal to 150 m on the baseline. The baselines are typically some 8000 km (5000 miles) in length and the lanes of a given station pair do not expand by more than a factor of about 2 in the region served by that pair.

Owing to the length of the baselines, earth curvature causes the Omega LOPs to depart from hyperbolic form. This can be understood by imagining a pattern generated by stations at opposite poles: the centre-line of the pattern would be an Equator with all other LOPs as parallels.

Position fixing

Depending on geometrical and other conditions, the position fix can be formed from the LOPs produced by two station pairs with a station common to each (this is the normal practice) or from two separate pairs. Usually a given chart carries only the patterns generated by stations deemed to be within range of the charted area. The eight stations provide a possible 28 different pairs but generally there are seldom more than four pairs, and in some places only two, within usable range. One of the constraints in the choice of LOPs is that the signals from a station nearer to the receiver than about 900 km are likely to be unreliable on a long-term basis owing to certain propagation effects.

Transmitting stations

The stations are listed in Table 4. The necessary synchronism in time and phase is achieved by the use of atomic-reference oscillators at each station. The size of the transmitting antenna systems is such that routine maintenance takes a relatively long time and accordingly each station is assigned a specific month in which to shut down.

Table 4   Omega station data (1986)

Ident.	Region/State	Place	Month for Maintenance
A	Norway	Aldra	August
B	Liberia	Monrovia	April
C	Hawaii	Haiku	June
D	N. Dakota	La Moure	July
E	Indian Ocean	Reunion Is.	September
F	Argentina	Golfo Neuvo	March
G	Australia	Woodside, Victoria	November
H	Japan	Tsushima	October

Accuracy (general)

The quality of Omega coverage varies considerably in different parts of the world, due to several factors. These include the effect of land masses (particularly in the Arctic) which the signals traverse, and the large variations in the level of radio noise as between tropical and temperate regions. In consequence the number of usable LOPs from which to form a position fix varies in different parts of the world from four or five to the necessary minimum of two.

There are however large areas, such as the South Atlantic Ocean bounded by approximately 20N–35S latitude and 70W–20E longitude, where extensive tests have shown that Omega meets the safety of navigation accuracy requirements of 2–4 nautical miles with 95% confidence. In northern European waters, where overland paths from the stations have a marked effect, calculations and practical observations have suggested rule-of-thumb figures of about 2.5 km (Drms) if corrections are applied by reference to the published data, and generally no better than about 9 km (Drms) in the absence of corrections.

Diurnal propagation variations

The main source of error in the Omega position fix is the daily (diurnal) variation in the effective speed of signal propagation, which corrupts the

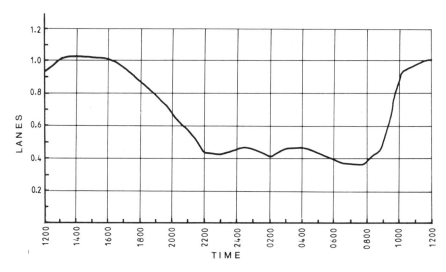

Fig. 30 Example of Omega LOP variation over 24 h.

time-difference measurement by the receiver. The variation in speed results from the difference in the height of the reflecting ionosphere by night from the height by day, bearing in mind that at vlf the ionosphere affects the signals throughout the 24 hours rather than mainly by night as with Decca. If uncorrected, the consequent variation in the LOP (see Fig.30) can reach a value of one lane or possibly more.

Omega Propagation Correction Tables are published by the US Defense Mapping Agency Hydrographic Center. Expressed in hundredths of a cycle (centicycles) against date and time (GMT), the corrections are published for a number of different areas and for each station individually. In considering a station pair, say AB, the convention is used that the receiver derives the phase difference (i.e. the LOP reading) by subtracting the phase of the signal identified by the higher letter from that identified by the lower. Thus if the tables showed corrections of −47 for A and −36 for B, the correction to apply to the AB LOP would be (−47) − (−36) = −11 centicycles. (Centicycles are compatible with centilanes and the former refer to the phase of an individual signal as opposed to a phase-difference.)

In Fig.30 it can be seen that at around dawn and dusk the ionospheric height is in a state of rapid transition, with the result that applying corrections has little value at these times. The transition from the day to the night condition or vice versa can take place in as short a time as one hour, which represents too rapid a rate of change for corrections to be effective. Between the transition periods, propagation conditions tend in general to be more stable by day than by night. Definition of dawn and dusk is complicated by the length and orientation of the three (minimum) or four transmission paths involved in an Omega fix; on E–W or W–E paths the dawn or dusk condition at a given time will apply only to a portion of the path.

Differential Omega

A feature of the Omega signals is that variations of the kind just described tend to be correlated in receivers as far apart as (say) 200 km. This enables a land-based station equipped with a receiver to broadcast real-time corrections to shipping in a wide area around the station, considerably improving the accuracy of the ships' position fixing. Some 14 of these 'Differential Omega' stations have been established, in Newfoundland, the Azores, France, Spain, N.W. Africa and the Caribbean.

Rendezvous performance

The rendezvous accuracy, defined in Chapter 2, of Omega is in general several times better than that of an individual position fix since the often large LOP fluctuations observed on the two ships increasingly tend to cancel out as the separation distance closes.

Other propagation anomalies

A variety of largely unpredictable propagation effects can cause LOP errors possibly amounting to a lane or more. These include sudden ionospheric disturbances (SIDs) associated with solar flares; interference between different modes of propagation within the waveguide formed by the earth and the ionosphere; the effects of transpolar signal paths (polar cap absorption or PCA); effects associated with the electrical characteristics of certain types of terrain on the signal paths, as already mentioned; and the varying influence of the earth's magnetic field depending on the direction of signal propagation.

While one of the merits of combining Omega with Transit is that the Transit fixes set a limit to the long-term accumulation of errors due to the causes listed above, some of these (especially SIDs) can introduce an LOP error of a lane or more within a time that is short compared with the typical interval between usable Transit fixes. It is therefore essential to monitor the Omega position frequently and to investigate any sudden divergence between the course made good, derived from Omega fixes, and that derived on a DR basis from the compass and log.

Lane ambiguity

At the 10.2 kHz frequency the lanes are about 15 km wide on the baselines and expand to about twice that width elsewhere. In principle, therefore, the user may need to know his position to within plus/minus 7.5 km in order to set up the receiver correctly, as described in Chapter 3. As the voyage proceeds the receiver will keep count of the lanes passed through, resolving the ambiguity so long as signal reception remains satisfactory. Under noisy or anomalous conditions the lane-count can be supported by DR, either manually or automatically depending on the type of receiver, reducing the likelihood of the user having to call upon some external source of position data to resolve the ambiguity. When the Omega position is updated by every usable Transit fix the problem of lane ambiguity is further reduced, except perhaps in the event of an unusually long interval between Transit fixes.

Lane identification

To resolve the lane ambiguity independently of the receiver's lane count, the Omega transmission sequence includes signals on several different frequencies in addition to 10.2 kHz. Most of the receivers suitable for small craft receive only the 10.2 kHz signals but some also have a 13.6 kHz channel. Combining the 10.2 and 13.6 kHz signals has the effect of superimposing on the 10.2 kHz lanes a coarse pattern having lanes three times wider (in other words, a lane pattern resulting from comparing signal phase at 13.6 − 10.2 = 3.4 kHz).

The coarse pattern coincides with the every-third-lane pattern that is printed on charts (Fig.29) and the lane identification readout on the receiver is numbered accordingly. Some receivers, however, display instead the LOPs produced by the 13.6 kHz pattern and this readout can serve to identify the correct 10.2 kHz lane in a known group of three by the method shown in Fig.31.

Omega Reference Epoch

The Omega frequencies are shared between the eight stations in a sequence comprising eight segments. The sequence repeats exactly every 10 s. The instant at which the first segment in the sequence starts is termed the Omega Reference Epoch or ORE and occurs on the minute in the International Atomic Time scale and on seconds 10, 20, 30 etc. IAT. There is however an internationally agreed offset, expressed in leap seconds, between IAT and GMT/UTI which on 30 June 1985 was increased from 12 to 13 seconds. Omega users should check *Notices to*

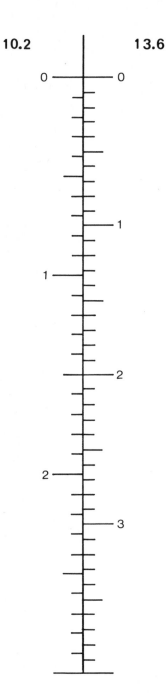

10.2   **13.6**   **Use of a 13.6 kHz lane fraction to check a 10.2 kHz lane number**

1. Suppose the receiver gives a 10.2 LOP reading of 937.2 but the lane number is in doubt.
2. Find the nearest number divisible by 3 below the lane number, subtract it from the LOP (937.2 − 936 = 1.2).
3. Enter 1.2 in the 10.2 scale and read the 13.6 value with which it coincides (1.6).
4. Read the displayed 13.6 lane fraction from the same station pair. If this is 1.6 it confirms the 10.2 lane number as 937. 13.6 readings of 0.27 or 0.93 would indicate, respectively, lanes 936 or 938.
5. The 10.2 and 13.6 readings are unlikely to coincide exactly as above, but there should be one value in the 10.2 scale that approaches the 13.6 reading more closely than the other two and this will identify the 10.2 lane within the known group of three.

   If after several attempts there is no clear choice, propagation conditions are such that lane identification is not possible.
6. Diurnal corrections should not be applied in this procedure.

Fig. 31 A method of Omega lane identification.

Mariners or similar sources for changes in the offset value. Inserting the leap seconds value into a processor-controlled receiver brings the receiver into near synchronism with the 10 s sequence and this can considerably reduce the time the receiver takes to acquire the signals.

Omega and Transit

It is as a partner for Transit that Omega has come into its own as a marine navigational aid. The periodic Transit fixes serve to update the relatively inaccurate Omega position while the nominally continuous Omega input helps to determine the velocity of the craft with the accuracy necessary for limiting the errors in the Transit fix (see next chapter). Processor software has been developed which turns the Omega/Transit combination, aided by DR inputs from compass and log, into a global navigational aid with an accuracy that is surpassed only in good Decca or Loran coverage.

Warning notices

Notification of planned changes in the Omega service, and reports of signal outages, are issued through similar channels to those for Decca (see Chapter 4). Each Omega station is closed down for maintenance during a specific month, indicated in the station list above.

Lattice charts

Marine charts overprinted with the Omega patterns are published by the Hydrographic Center of the US Defense Mapping Agency (DMA) and by agencies in Europe. Tables are published which define the LOPs as a succession of lat/long positions, enabling users to superimpose the Omega grid on unlatticed charts.

Publications on Omega

In the USA a book entitled *Omega Global Navigation – a Guide for Users* is published by the US Government Printing Office, Washington DC 20402.

7
Transit

Origin and status

The US Navy Navigation Satellite System (NNSS), more widely known as Transit, was developed for the US Navy by the Applied Physics Laboratory of the Johns Hopkins University. Experimental satellites were launched in the early 1960s and the system became operational in 1964. A few years later the first commercial receivers became available. Initially these were cumbersome and expensive owing to the complexity and volume of the computations involved in deriving the position fix from the satellite signals. In the 1970s the development of the microprocessor led to radical reductions in the size, cost and power consumption of the shipboard equipment and Transit is now extensively used by small craft.

Transit is operated by the Department of the Navy, US Department of Defense. It combines global coverage, potentially high accuracy and proven reliability to a degree that is unmatched by any aid to marine navigation based on terrestrial transmitters. The penalties for this performance are a generally long interval between fixes and a critical dependence upon accurate knowledge of the user craft's velocity over the ground. Transit is a valuable navigational aid for sea-going craft of all kinds, operating anywhere in the world, but because of the time between fixes it is less effective for coastal navigation than Decca or Loran, which provide continuous fixing in their respective areas of coverage.

In contrast with the other systems described in this book, judgements as to the viability of the position fix are left to the on-board processor. It is a paradox that the extreme simplicity (for the user) of Transit in its modern form may even be helping to breed an uncritical attitude towards navigation in general: the claim has already appeared in print that with a Transit receiver 'you will be confident of knowing exactly where you are regardless'.

Configuration

A single 'pass' by an individual Transit satellite serves to fix the user's position provided that it meets certain conditions noted later. Five satellites are in operation (May 1986), together with a 'rogue' and some non-transmitting reserves. They travel in near-circular orbit about 1100 km above the earth. The orbits pass over the poles but the orbital plane tends to precess or drift slowly in longitude with the result that the orbits are not evenly spaced. A Transit satellite takes about 107 minutes to circle the earth.

The coverage area of an individual satellite forms a strip (Fig.32) roughly 6000 km wide, the width of the strip being set by the minimum angle of elevation of the satellite above the user's horizon that is acceptable for an effective fix. Because the earth is rotating, at 15 deg/h, the sub-satellite track on the earth's surface does not run due north or south.

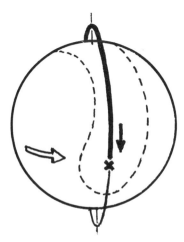

Fig. 32 Transit satellite orbit and coverage strip.

Fundamental to the Transit system is the network of fixed tracking stations (currently four) located at accurately known positions in the USA. These stations compile precise data on the observed orbit of each satellite so as to predict its future orbits over the following 16 hours. Two of the stations have the function of uploading the memory in the processor carried by each satellite by transmitting, approximately every 12 hours, a fresh set of predicted orbital data.

On the basis of the memorised data, each satellite broadcasts, every 2 minutes exactly, a 'navigation message' which in effect defines the satellite's own position in space at a specified instant. The message includes precise time data and the satellite identity number, and comprises a total of 6103 digital bits occupying the full 2 min. interval. The navigation message is transmitted on carrier frequencies of approximately 400 MHz and 150 MHz, although most of the receivers intended for navigational use (as opposed to geodetic work) employ only the 400 MHz signal. The two frequencies combine to make possible the correction of certain small errors which result from the passage of the signals through the ionosphere.

Principle

By receiving the radio signal from the satellite throughout its pass from horizon to horizon, which takes from 10 to 20 minutes depending on the user's proximity to the sub-satellite track, the user's receiver obtains a succession of navigation messages and it also continuously measures the Doppler frequency shift on the received radio signal. From the satellite positions supplied by the navigation messages and from the values and rate of change of the Doppler shift (the 'Doppler history') the receiver is able to compute, once the pass is complete, the position of the user craft in latitude and longitude.

Doppler

The frequency shift phenomenon which was first described, in reference to light waves, by the Austrian mathematician and physicist Christian Doppler (1803–1853) occurs when the distance between the receiver and the source of a wave transmission is changing due to their relative motion. Neglecting effects due to relativity and gravitation that are too small to matter here, the Doppler shift boils down to the very simple relationship

$$F_D = +/- v/\lambda$$

where F_D is the difference in Hz between the received and transmitted frequencies,

v is the rate at which the transmitter-to-receiver distance is changing, and

λ is the wavelength of the transmission.

The shift is positive when the distance is closing, negative when it is increasing. The formula can be shown to support the statement made about receiver movement in Chapter 3.

Thus when the distance between transmitter and receiver is not changing ($v = 0$), the same number of cycles will arrive at the receiver during a given time as were transmitted in that time (zero frequency shift). When there is relative motion such that the distance is closing, the rate of closure will be added to the speed of wave propagation with the result that successive cycles will be received at a higher rate in the given time (positive or upward frequency shift). When the distance is increasing, fewer cycles will arrive at the receiver in that time (downward or negative shift). As the above formula shows, the wavelength does not change: if it did, systems such as Omega and Decca would be unworkable since their lane-width depends directly on wavelength.

Examples of 'Doppler history'

A rough idea of the relationship between the doppler shift on the Transit signal and the position of the observing receiver (and of how scientists in the West used the radio signal from Sputnik to determine its orbit) can be gained from the Doppler histories sketched in Fig.33.

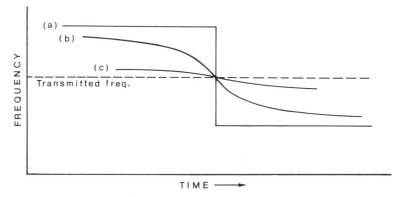

Fig. 33 Notional Doppler histories.
(a) Transmitter passing through observing position. (b) Transit pass (approximate). (c) Distant Transit pass.

Curve (a) shows the fortunately impossible case of a low-flying satellite passing straight over (indeed *through*) the receiver: plotted against time, the received frequency of its radio signal is constant at an upward-shifted value during the approach and changes instantly to a negative value as the transmitter passes the receiver. If this were a Transit satellite, its track would be running almost north-south and its navigation messages would enable the receiver to compute the satellite's latitude at the instant of the change of sign in the Doppler shift; this in turn would give the receiver its own latitude at that instant.

The suddenness of the change of sign in case (a) would tell the receiver that the satellite passed very close to its own position and that therefore the longitude of the receiver must have been virtually that of the satellite itself (deduced from the navigation message) at the instant of the frequency-change.

Because of the height of the satellite orbit above the earth, the Doppler sign-change is never so sudden as in (a) and in practice a typical

Doppler history is more like curve (b). Curve (c) shows that when the satellite is distant from the user craft, such that it rises only to a small angle of elevation during the pass, it will be 'in view' for a relatively short time; the extent of the Doppler shift will be relatively small and the transition from positive to negative very gradual. One can therefore say in crude terms that the passing of the Doppler shift through zero gives the user his latitude and the rate of change or slope of the curve at that point gives his longitude.

It turns out on closer examination, however, that Transit is a hyperbolic system. By counting the number of Doppler-frequency cycles received between one announcement of the satellite's position and the next, the receiver computes the difference in the distance from the craft to the two satellite positions. Such positions follow in succession during the pass and can be likened to a chain of Decca or Loran stations in space, fixing the user's position on the earth by the intersection of surfaces (hyperboloids) on which distance-differences are constant. Three-dimensional paper would be required to illustrate this properly.

Position fixing

The interval of time between successive position fixes of the user craft depends on the number of satellites in service and on the latitude. The interval is shortest at the poles, over which all the satellites pass, and longest on the Equator where it approaches 2 hours on the average. In UK latitudes the average interval is about 1½ hours. Because of the variable spacing between the orbits, the interval between usable passes at a given position varies correspondingly; occasionally several hours may elapse between fixes and it can also happen that two or possibly more satellites rise over the user's horizon at about the same time. Most Transit receivers predict the times of future passes, as described later.

Accuracy

Using a single-frequency Transit receiver a position fix accurate to within ± 0.1 n.mile (180 m) can be obtained in most circumstances from a satisfactory pass, assuming that the all-important condition is met of supplying the receiver with an accurate input of the craft's velocity over the ground. Since the fix is based on the Doppler frequency shift which in turn depends on the rate of change in the transmitter-to-receiver distance, it follows that the receiver's own velocity (speed and course) contributes to that rate of change. Less obvious, perhaps, is the fact that although the satellite travels at 7.3 km/s (about 4 n.miles per second), an error of one knot in specifying the speed of a craft cruising at (say) 10 kt may have the effect of more than doubling the error in the Transit fix.

Effect of craft's velocity

For every knot by which the velocity of the craft over the ground inserted in the Transit receiver is in error, the position fix is liable to be in error by up to an additional 0.2 n.mile (368 m). The added fix error will be largest when the craft is on a northerly or southerly course, i.e. sailing approximately parallel to the satellite's track, and least when heading east or west. Once a pass has started and the receiver has acquired the signals, an attempt to amend or refine the velocity entry is likely to add to the error. The course and speed of the craft should be held as constant as possible throughout the pass.

Because of the importance of an accurate velocity input, Transit receivers include a DR facility based, as a minimum, upon keyed-in entries of heading and speed. Most receivers accept inputs from a range of different types of repeater compass and speed log, and provide for the manual entry of tidal drift and set with which to refine the velocity computed from the DR. An associated Omega receiver can provide velocity data of useful quality between Transit fixes, particularly if it is in turn supported during periods of unstable reception by a DR input from compass and log.

Effect of high or low pass

Returning to the basic Transit position fix, accuracy is degraded if the maximum angle of elevation that the satellite reaches during a pass, with respect to the user craft, is less than 10° or greater than 80°. Consideration of the polar orbit and the Doppler measurement will make it clear that a satellite passing directly over the craft will in principle give an accurate latitude but a relatively poor longitude whereas a fix from a pass that is low over the horizon will be better in longitude than in latitude. Transit receivers issue a warning, in one form or another, when a pass is 'high' or 'low' and may reject it as a basis for fix computation: the *User's Manual* for the receiver will give data on this.

Prediction of future passes

Once a Transit receiver has computed the position of the craft from a satellite signal, it will have accumulated sufficient data on that particular satellite's orbit to be able to predict the times of future orbits of the same satellite that will be observable from the position concerned. Some receivers can predict on this basis the next 100 passes (or perhaps more) of a given satellite that will be observable, from a given date, at any specified point on the earth. This is a useful aid to voyage planning although a limit of 2 months ahead is advised since the accuracy of prediction tends to decrease with time.

Each prediction typically comprises the satellite identity number, time of rise, maximum elevation angle and direction of rise. When the receiver has been running for some hours and has computed fixes from several or all the satellites in orbit, it will display their future passes in time order.

Warning notices

The reliability of the Transit system as a whole, and of the individual satellites, one of which has been in orbit and functioning perfectly for more than 19 years, represents such a formidable engineering achievement that mention of warning notices here seems almost out of order. For the record, however, announcements concerning the system are made through channels such as those used for Decca (Chapter 4).

Transit and GPS

It has long been realised that the problem of the interval between Transit fixes, and that of the dependence on knowing the user craft's velocity, could both be eliminated by adopting a different type of system. Such a system, which also gives three-dimensional fixing for aircraft and spacecraft, has been duly developed by the US Department of Defense under the names GPS (Global Positioning System) and NavStar, and has been operating experimentally for some years.

GPS was provisionally scheduled to become operational in 1988 and to replace Transit by 1994. The extent of the delay in this schedule imposed by the problems with the launch vehicle cannot be forecast at the time of writing but there are grounds for believing that it may not amount to more than a year or two. Using 18 satellites, GPS will provide position-fixing at two levels of accuracy through a Precise Positioning Service (PPS) encoded for military use and a lower-accuracy Standard Positioning Service (SPS) available to civilian users. Maritime users of the SPS element in its final form will probably be able to fix their position anywhere in the world, at any time, with an accuracy in the order of 100 metres. Shipboard equipment for use with GPS is already available commercially.

The 18 satellites will move around the earth in orbital planes so chosen that at least four will be 'in view' from a given spot at any time. They will be much higher than those of Transit, taking some 12 hours to circle the earth. The signals from three satellites will suffice to give a shipboard user his latitude and longitude; four will give a 3D fix for air and space craft. GPS as a whole is extremely sophisticated and receiver operation will be virtually automatic, but the form of the position fix can be roughly illustrated, as with Transit, by regarding the GPS satellites as hyperbolic stations announcing their own positions and sending signals from whose TDs the shipboard receiver derives distance differences.

Referring back to Fig. 7, suppose the plane containing the three stations is suspended in space with the stations roughly equidistant from the earth. Taking as a simple example the centre-lines of the two patterns, it will be clear that each centre-line lies in a flat plane everywhere on which the distance difference to two of the stations is zero. The centre-planes will intersect, so creating a position line running down to the earth; if a ship's GPS receiver/processor observed that the two TDs were in fact each equal to zero, it would give the position as the point where the downcoming position line (as just defined) cuts the earth's surface.

Distance differences other than zero correspond to solid figures or hyperboloids of rotation about the baseline, whose profile is indicated by the lattice lines in the diagram. In 3D their typical shape somewhat resembles that of a headlight reflector. To summarise, GPS fixes a ship's position as the point where a (generally curved) position line defined by two position surfaces cuts the surface of the earth.

8
Equipment Features

Introduction

In the foregoing chapters the hyperbolic position fixing systems were considered simply as sensors from which LOPs, and hence a fix, were obtained. Similarly Transit was described only with reference to the basic determination of position. The present generation of shipboard receivers for the different systems have various additional features, some of which are briefly outlined below.

The word 'receiver' is taken here and in the following chapter to comprise radio receiving channel(s) together with a processor, displays and keyboard. Generally all are housed in a single unit.

The microprocessor revolution

Until about the mid-1970s Decca, Loran and Omega were used on board ships mainly by plotting the LOPs, which were all that the receivers then supplied, on a lattice chart. Simple automatic plotters had been in use for some time although more for purposes such as fishing than for general navigation. The arrival of the microprocessor, a name that explains itself, allowed complex computations to be performed by equipment that was a fraction of the size demanded by previous technology as well as being cheaper, more reliable and consuming less power.

The microprocessor made hyperbolic position fixing a practical proposition for small craft and it enabled the shipboard receivers to embody features that had long been seen as desirable although impracticable. Foremost among these was the transformation of the hyperbolic fix into latitude and longitude; as well as enhancing the display of position, this provided a uniform, earth-related system of co-ordinates upon which positional computations could be based (e.g. for waypoints, and for 'integrating' or combining position fixing data from different sources). Without the microprocessor Transit would not have become viable for small craft and the same applies to peripheral equipment such as today's video plotters.

Automatic operation

For each of the systems, receiver operation has become largely automatic. For example, receivers of the multi-sensor type store data enabling them to determine, at any specified position, whether Decca, Loran or Omega is the best hyperbolic 'sensor' to use. Having made this choice, the receiver selects the best chain to use and acquires the signals automatically. Less elaborate receivers operating with a single hyperbolic sensor similarly select the best chain on the basis of stored data, and the correct LOP patterns to use for the fix. With some receivers the choice of patterns is automatic irrespective of whether the chain is selected automatically or manually.

Changing chains

When the coverage areas of two adjacent chains overlap (assuming that these are both Decca chains or both Loran) and the user craft travels from one coverage area to the other, the receiver will automtically switch to the 'new' chain at some point in the overlap area. A degree of so-called hysteresis (delay) can be built in whereby the change does not take place until the processor calculates that the accuracy of the new chain exceeds that of the old by some predetermined margin; if the craft were then to go about and return to the old chain, re-acquisition of the signals from that chain would be delayed until it was calculated to be giving the better fix.

Filtering

The following paragraphs refer to hyperbolic receivers (i.e. not Transit) and are concerned with the problem of filtering or extracting the required phase information from potentially noisy radio signals, whether these are Omega or Decca cw transmissions or Loran-C carrier waves. Digital processing has brought important advances in this field by allowing operations to be performed upon the incoming signals of a speed and complexity that no human observer could hope to emulate. (It should be added in passing, however, that no computer program yet exists that can match an experienced user's judgements as to the implications of, say, a fluctuating LOP readout in given circumstances and of what, if anything, to do about it.)

To use a not too inaccurate analogy, the effect of such filtering may be likened to interposing flywheels in the mechanism driving the latitude and longitude displays of the present position, giving the readings a certain inertia in their response to the incoming LOPs.

Filtering is quantified in terms of time; when signal quality is good a 'time constant' of a few seconds may be sufficient to protect the position display from any small but sudden changes in the LOPs that occur, while allowing it to respond quite rapidly to the new rates of change of signal phase that will result when the craft alters course. A much longer time constant (tens of seconds) may be necessary under conditions causing severe fluctuations of the LOPs and/or in order to limit unnecessary rudder activity when the position fixing receiver is coupled to an autopilot (see next chapter).

The effect of filtering upon the displayed position is such that when the craft starts to turn, the inertia prevents the display responding for some time, with the result that the apparent track runs wide of the true one. When the craft has settled down on the new course, the apparent position will take time to 'catch up', depending on the value of the time constant. If, however, the receiver is one which accepts a continuous input of heading from the compass, it can compute the rate of change of heading and use this to override in a large measure the lagging effect of the filter.

Video plotter

Many owners of small craft will be concerned to minimise the amount of equipment installed on board, consistent with their navigational preferences. However, where size, power consumption and cost are not critical a video plotter will add the considerable advantage of a pictorial display of the present position, and if required of the track made good, against a background of chart detail and waypoint positions.

Video plotters are so called because the chart detail is generated and stored electronically and is viewed on a cathode ray tube display. The technique allows simple operation (e.g. by means of a light pen rather than a keyboard) to be combined with features such as the use of colour to distinguish, say, tracks from coastlines; the display, on demand, of the Mercator grid for any area of the world, given an entry of the lat/long position of the centre-point of the area; and two-way transfer of data whereby waypoints can be entered *en bloc* from a receiver or from a disk cassette for display on the chart, or extracted *en bloc* from the plotter for storage externally.

Interfaces

Position fixing receivers can drive various peripheral devices including automatic pilots and printers as well as plotters. Most such devices accept the position input from the receiver in the form of serial binary messages (streams of noughts and ones) and these messages have to conform to a standard format so as to ensure compatibility between different types of receiver and peripheral device. The circuit in the receiver that organises the output data into the correct format and forms the link between the receiver and the device is known as an interface.

Receiver specifications refer to the interfaces in terms such as RS232 and NMEA 0180. The former term covers a range of specifications for the electrical characteristics. The National Marine Electronics Association of the USA (NMEA) has developed a series of standards, accepted internationally, which lay down the structure and format of messages between marine navigational devices. An NMEA standard often encountered is known as the 0180 Simple format which relates to the displacement from a specific track (i.e. across-track error), for example in an autopilot control signal. NMEA 0183 covers the format of the more comprehensive messages between receivers and peripheral devices such as certain types of autopilot, plotter, printer and data terminal.

Power supply

Position fixing receivers operate from d.c. supplies in the range 9–36 V (sometimes 10–42 V). Some also accept an a.c. supply in the range 110–220 V, although a separate rectifier unit is more usual. Power consumption is usually between the limits of 4 W and 12 W but the multi-sensor type of receiver may consume about 60 W.

Data protection

Provision is made in processor-based equipment for preserving at least the contents of the 'volatile' memory, such as waypoint positions entered in the course of operation, when the power supply is interrupted accidentally or otherwise. This will consist of a small internal battery with a nominal life reckoned in the order of months or more usually years. Some receivers display the time at which the supply was last interrupted in order to assist the estimation of present position on resuming operation after an accidental power cut.

Built-in tests

All receivers now include provision for a range of tests, initiated from the keyboard, which combine to exercise a large part of the equipment. Under normal conditions some of these tests are in the nature of confidence-checks. Others are designed to identify faults and locate the source. Tests of the display system commonly include a moving 'parade' of all the characters involved in the displays so that they occupy in turn each of the character spaces, and this has the additional merit of helping a new user to gain familiarity with the characters and symbols employed. No tests should however be initiated without first consulting the *User's Manual*, since there may be some that incur the loss of stored data.

9
Navigation Facilities

Introduction

Some of the navigational facilities now provided by position fixing receivers for the hyperbolic systems and/or for Transit, are discussed below. Not all of these facilities are necessarily obtainable from a given receiver. Different makes and types of receiver vary in many respects, including the terminology used.

Latitude and longitude

All the modern receivers display the present position of the craft in latitude and longitude and some also display the hyperbolic LOPs. The convenience of a lat/long display is obvious, for example in its compatibility with conventional marine charts, but there goes with it a possible pitfall that should be mentioned. This stems from the fact that a reading in the time-honoured co-ordinates of latitude and longitude, often to a resolution of 0.01 minute, seems to strike people as carrying a sort of built-in authenticity:

050 41.49 N 001 17.56 W

The effect is compounded by the knowledge that one's pocket calculator never makes mistakes of its own, even when handling quite large numbers, so surely (the thinking seems to go) such a reading must be OK.

A different but related reaction is remembered from the time when a certain Establishment acquired an early type of digital computer to use with the Decca receiver in a helicopter employed on flight trials. Part of the trials procedure was to take the aircraft to a well-surveyed point X, on the ground. There was known to be a fixed error there in one of the Decca patterns and this had long been allowed for. The new computer had a lat/long readout and soon after it was installed the Decca Company received a telephone call. 'There must be something wrong', a voice said, 'the latitude is way out at X'. Gloom at the receiving end (not *another* software bug?) – but it turned out to be nothing more than the same fixed error. Accepted readily enough when expressed as a fraction of a Decca lane, the error was somehow unthinkable in terms of latitude.

Warning indications

Receiver manufacturers soon realised that they would have to take steps to keep the user in touch with the actual conditions underlying this unimpeachable-looking display of the present position. A digital readout offers no counterpart to the 'wobble' of a meter-pointer (such as that of a Decometer) which can tell an experienced user a lot about the quality of the incoming information; a jumping least-significant digit tends to be regarded as just an irritant on a digital display.

Accordingly most, if not all, hyperbolic receivers provide an on-demand display of the Drms value, or a near equivalent, together with the direction of worst fix. Indications of signal quality (signal:noise ratio) are provided, typically as a 0 to 9 grading. It is usual for a warning symbol such as an asterisk to appear on position and other displays, possibly accompanied by an audible alarm, when the processor detects certain substandard conditions.

Discrepancies between receivers

At least so far as the Decca system is concerned, different makes of receiver may display different lat/long readings at a given location. One reason for this is that certain receivers have been designed without reference to Racal-Decca and hence without access to data, accumulated from monitor stations and elsewhere over the years, on the propagation and general behaviour of the signals. One such receiver appears to embody a non-optimum value of propagation speed which is a basic parameter in the co-ordinate conversion. Another makes no allowance for the modification, on certain chains, to the slave phasing that the operating authorities have made in order to adjust the geographical distribution of fixed error values as described in Chapter 4.

Different co-ordinates, same fix

It is easy to overlook the fact that a position fix displayed by a hyperbolic receiver in the uniform co-ordinate system of latitude and longitude, or for that matter in terms such as the bearing and distance to a waypoint, is nevertheless subject to the variations and error distribution described in Chapter 2. The message of Fig.12 invariably applies when fixes are derived from hyperbolic LOPs, no matter what form the actual display may take.

Geodetic datum

Latitude and longitude relate to a specific figure of the earth (geoid). Computations associated with Transit are based on a reference geoid known as WGS72 (World Geodetic System) and in general this can be used in the hyperbolic-to-lat/long conversion without significant error so far as normal navigation is concerned. Charts covering different regions are, however, based on a variety of different geodetic data although they often carry an indication of the correction to be applied when plotting a position computed on the basis of WGS72. In order to ensure direct compatibility with such charts, some receivers offer a choice, via the keyboard, of several national geodetic data in addition to WGS72 on which to base the co-ordinate conversion.

The Ghost Buoy

Once it has performed the conversion to lat/long, the processor in the receiver can readily compute the range and bearing from the present position of the user craft to any point whose position has previously been stored in the processor memory. The operational possibilities that would follow from this had been appreciated long before the arrival of the microprocessor; an early attempt, using an electro-mechanical computer, was aptly named the Ghost Buoy to emphasise the (then) novel idea that the specified point need not coincide with the position of any actual object or feature. The waypoint, as it became called, was a major contribution of electronics to navigation.

Waypoint definition

Almost every radio position fixing receiver has a waypoint facility. The position of a waypoint can in principle be entered in any one of the four forms shown in Fig.34, namely in latitude and longitude; as a range and bearing from the present position of the craft; as a range and bearing from another waypoint already stored; and in hyperbolic LOPs. Some receivers offer all four methods of definition. Once the waypoint has been entered, say, in lat/long, the processor will display its position in the other forms as well as generating steering and other data with respect to the waypoint as described later.

Waypoint storage

Each waypoint stored in the processor memory is assigned an identity number, so that by keying in that number the user obtains a display of the range, bearing, etc. of the waypoint. Mainly because of the variety of functions that waypoints can perform there is an ongoing demand for greater storage capacity and 100 is now not unusual. There have even

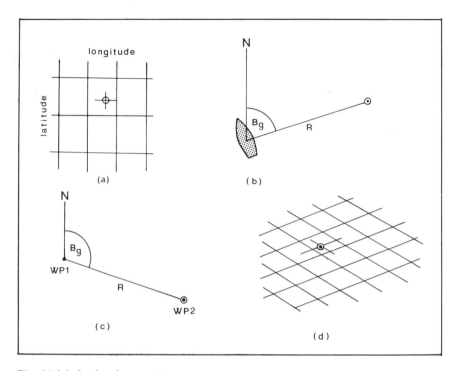

Fig. 34 Methods of waypoint entry.
(a) Lat/long. (b) Range/bearing from craft. (c) Range/bearing from an existing waypoint WP1. (d) Hyperbolic LOPs.

been serious requests for a waypoint capacity of 1000, possibly without due appreciation of the chore involved in keying them all in. It has latterly become feasible to transfer *en bloc* the contents of a receiver's waypoint store to, say, a video plotter which will then display them as symbols on the 'chart'.

Position marking

The uses for waypoints will of course depend on individual circumstances. A new user would be wise to start by establishing a waypoint at the position of each buoy, coastal feature and so on that he relies upon in good visibility around his home port or on habitual cruising grounds; to be able to find the range, more accurately than one can generally judge it visually, and the bearing to a mark that has become obscured in the haze (or is invisible to a radar if fitted) is a facility well worth having. And so, of course, is the ability to deploy Ghost Buoys of one's own at will in waters devoid of real ones. The 1987 edition of the *Macmillan & Silk Cut Nautical Almanac* gives almost 1500 lat/long positions of harbours, buoys, etc. in north and west Europe for use as waypoints.

Certain waypoint-related warning (bleeper) signals are normally provided, for example when the distance to the waypoint ahead falls to a pre-set value. An anchor-watch or drift warning operates if the distance from a waypoint defining the position at anchor should exceed a pre-set limit. The steering data mentioned below may also be subject to warning signals when pre-set limits are exceeded.

Waypoints as marker buoys

Most receivers allow the user to perform at will the electronic equivalent of dropping a marker buoy at a point of interest, by pressing a single key. The processor will then store the position of the craft at that instant as a waypoint, and will thereafter display, on demand, steering and range data for recovering that position. This is sometimes called an auto waypoint. Provision may be included for creating an auto waypoint by pressing a 'man overboard' alarm button, which will also give display priority to the rapid recovery of the position.

Calibrated waypoints

In parts of the USA, Loran-C TD readings have been observed and published for certain key positions which are likely. to be used as waypoints. For example, in the Delaware Bay and River, New York Harbour, and the St Mary River these are positions where the centre-lines of ship channels intersect or where a centre-line is marked by a buoy. In principle the published data enables Loran users to establish waypoints at such positions with the virtual elimination of fixed errors as defined in Chapter 2. The data include TDs observed at certain positions known as trackpoints, along the channels between intersections, with the object of minimising across-track errors.

By the same token, when establishing a waypoint at, say, the actual position of a buoy, the effect of a local fixed error can be removed by observing the displayed present position of the craft when close to the buoy in question and entering that position as the waypoint, rather than simply taking the buoy position off a chart.

Steering to a waypoint

An intended route can be defined by waypoints marking the turning points between successive legs. Since there is no restriction as to where the turning points are placed (except for that imposed by the quality of the local coverage of the hyperbolic chain in use) an optimum route can be planned with consequent savings of time and fuel under power. When under sail a route so defined will bear a flexible interpretation but at least one item in the waypoint steering data may nevertheless be useful, as noted later.

Taking first the case of steering to an individual waypoint, the receiver will typically compute and display the type of data shown in Fig.35 and detailed below. The terms used may vary with different makes of receiver, as will the availability of options such as the choice of rhumb line or great circle computation of bearings and tracks. Receivers for the relatively short-range Decca system generally deal in rhumb lines only. ETA and time to go to the next waypoint are usually displayed in addition to the following data.

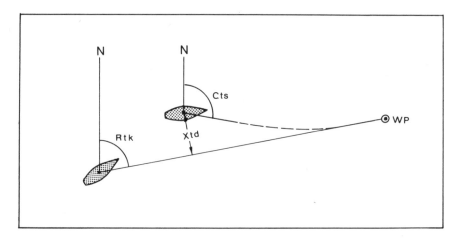

Fig. 35 Steering to a waypoint.
The computed Cts would normally take account of the tide vector, omitted here for clarity.

In Fig.35 the required track (Rtk) is the rhumb line or great circle, as selected, joining the waypoint to the position occupied by the craft at the instant of initiating the steering mode, expressed in degrees with respect to true north. The displayed Rtk will not therefore change as the craft moves.

Course to steer (Cts) is the course which, taking into account the velocity vector for the tidal stream, should bring the track made good smoothly into coincidence with the required track. Most receivers accept manual inputs of estimated tidal drift and set, and/or will derive mean values for these by comparing the track and speed made good (defined in a later paragraph) with inputs of heading and speed.

Across-track error (Xtd) is the distance of the craft to left or right of the required track, e.g. in n.miles up to 9.99. Under sail this display can be a useful aid to tacking.

Distance to go (Dtg) is self-explanatory in the case of an individual waypoint but may in some cases refer to the final waypoint in a series marking a route.

Route marking

A leg of an intended route may be defined by a waypoint at each end, in which case the required track Rtk then becomes the rhumb line or great circle joining the two waypoints and the craft is steered as above. A route comprising several legs can generally be set up in this way and some receivers will store a selection of such routes. There are two ways of handling the transition from one leg to the next.

Change of leg direction

On completing a leg and coming abeam of a waypoint marking a change of direction, the displays will generally be transferred automatically to the next waypoint ahead and the helmsman will alter course in response to the new Cts. (Some receivers effect the transfer on crossing the line bisecting the angle between the legs, rather than when abeam of the waypoint.)

Alternatively, a suitable receiver can anticipate the change of course and display a progressively changing Cts calculated to take the craft smoothly round the turn. In such a case the Cts starts to change at a point short of the waypoint by a distance that is a multiple of the 'ship length' which the user enters from the keyboard. The rate of change of the Cts will conform to a radius of turn equal to several times the ship length, finally decreasing as the new Rtk is approached. Transition to the next leg in this way lends itself to autopilot control when the control signal from the receiver is an electrical analogue of the Cts.

Steering note

When steering a craft to make good a waypoint-defined track, one could be excused for expecting the accuracy of the course-to-steer information to improve as the waypoint ahead is approached, just as a D/F bearing gets better as the distance to the transmitter decreases. There is however no basis for this in the waypoint case, unless it so happens that the waypoint ahead is in better hyperbolic coverage than the craft in her

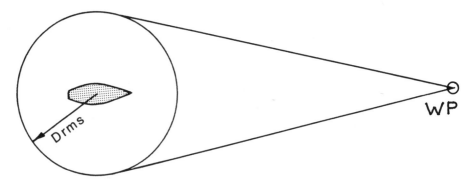

Fig. 36 Impossible task for the coupled autopilot.
Owing to position fixing variations (Drms) the apparent bearing of a
waypoint will vary increasingly as the waypoint is approached.

present position. The quality of the steering computation will, in fact
tend to deteriorate on approaching the waypoint ahead (see Fig.36) and
this is discussed further below.

Autopilots

An automatic pilot is a steering device which maintains the craft on a
selected course, normally using a magnetic or gyro directional sensor as
the basic reference. On probably the majority of pleasure craft that are
equipped with an autopilot and with a position fixing receiver, the two
are used as independent but complementary aids to navigation. The
user forms the link between them, periodically monitoring the track
made good by reference to the position display; when the trend of the
fixes indicates a significant deviation from the track required, an
appropriate trimming adjustment is made to the course set into the
autopilot. Many yachtsmen instinctively prefer to remain 'in the loop' in
this way.

   Given a receiver with a suitable interface, an autopilot can be directly
controlled by Decca or Loran position fixes. A widely used method of
control, limited to guidance along straight legs, retains the normal
heading reference for the autopilot which then adjusts the pre-set course
in response to distance-off-track signals from the receiver. In more
elaborate autopilots (and receivers) the control signal is an analogue of
the course to steer (Cts in Fig.35). In this case the control signal, so long
as it is operative, replaces the autopilot's heading reference and can
command a progressive course alteration to achieve a smooth transfer
from one leg to the next.

   Autopilot 'coupling' can give good results provided always that the
signal quality and the pattern geometry are good enough in the part of

the coverage concerned. When they are not, it soon becomes all too clear that the old computer catchphrase 'rubbish in, rubbish out' (US: garbage) applies with special force to the subject of coupling autopilots to radio position fixing receivers. If conditions are wrong, autopilot coupling can defeat two of its objects by increasing wear on the steering gear through excessive rudder activity and hence wasting fuel.

A glance at Fig.36 will make it clear that the variations, represented by Drms, in the present position derived by a hyperbolic receiver will cause the apparent bearing of a waypoint to vary to an extent that increases as the waypoint is approached. Simple trigonometry shows that when the distance falls to, say, 20 times the Drms value that the receiver is displaying, the waypoint bearing variations will amount to about plus/minus 3° for much of the time (remembering the statistical basis of Drms) and may occasionally exceed 10°. In such conditions the autopilot should be uncoupled from the receiver and used in the manual mode described earlier.

The term 'direct coupling' is used here to mean the generation of a control signal from radio position fixes. With a receiver that includes a DR mode of operation (see below), autopilot coupling is often more satisfactory in that mode because of the relatively small short-term errors in the compass and log inputs. Such a receiver will include provision for updating the DR by reference to the radio fixes, although this may call for temporary disconnection of the autopilot in order to avoid inflicting on it an unwanted 'data jump'. Before attempting autopilot coupling of any kind it is essential to study the relevant specifications and make certain that receiver and autopilot are fully compatible.

Track and speed made good

The continuous position fix provided by a hyperbolic system enables the receiver to compute and display the track and speed made good on the basis of successive fixes averaged over a certain time. In some receivers this process is closely linked to that of the filtering described in the previous chapter. The words 'course made good' are sometimes used in this context but what the measurement actually produces is the mean track and mean speed made good over the ground during the averaging time. That time is generally variable over a wide range, up to perhaps an hour or two. The accuracy increases with the averaging time provided a straight course is maintained, and falls as soon as course changes become large or frequent.

By comparing vectorially the track and speed made good with the change in DR position derived from heading and speed sensors over the same period, a vector representing the mean set and drift of the tidal stream is obtained. Some receivers can perform this calculation automatically. Its validity depends on the stability of the tidal conditions and in coastal waters it is better to enter estimated values for the tide vector from the keyboard. Receivers that include a DR mode generally provide for such entries so that an estimated position (EP) can be derived.

Dead reckoning

Many position fixing receivers, and especially those which include Transit as a sensor, accept inputs of heading and speed from a repeater-type compass and log or, failing these, from the keyboard as estimated values. Given such inputs and an initial position, the receiver continuously computes the DR position which can be upgraded to the EP as just stated. Basically the DR process is independent of, but complementary to, the radio position fix. It can serve to bridge gaps in radio reception and, being based on inputs that are relatively smooth in the short term, it provides a means of detecting and possibly correcting gross errors in the radio input such as lane or cycle jumps.

Implementation of the DR varies in different receivers. In at least one the EP and the hyperbolic fix are displayed side by side to help the user decide which is the more valid in given circumstances. Thus if the radio input were intermittent or suspect the EP would be accepted as the present position until reception improved and it could then be updated by pressing a single key. Some hyperbolic receivers initiate the DR only when signal quality falls below a predetermined threshold level, using the last-recorded fix as the starting position; with others it is the user who decides when to initiate DR.

Time-related displays

An accurate time source (calendar/clock) is embodied in all position fixing receivers. Omega signal acquisition is enhanced by the existence of suitably accurate time data in the receiver, future Transit passes are predicted in terms of time and date, and the Drms prediction in Decca receivers is time and date dependent. Most receivers compute ETA and time to go to the next waypoint. Other time-based functions include an alarm clock, a count-down readout for race starts, and fuel consumption computation given an input from a flow transducer. For sailing craft the Decca Yacht Navigator III includes a calculation of Vmg, based on the resolution of track and speed made good into up-wind and cross-wind components together with an entered wind direction.

Take care

Position fixing receivers process and deliver a large variety of data, calling for a corresponding variety of entries from the keyboard for setting-up and other purposes. This in turn has brought a much greater chance of human error than there was when the receivers dealt only in LOPs. The entry of waypoints offers particular scope for blunders. A common source of keying error is the habit (very easily acquired) of not looking at the display while, or after, keying in a sequence of digits. Another is neglect of (or over-dependence on) the fact that the display may 'default' to a particular state unless over-written from the keyboard. For example, displays accepting entries in lat/long commonly default to N and E and the error implications of this hardly need enlarging upon here.

At a recent Boat Show the author asked several manufacturers and suppliers of radio position fixing equipment what they now find to be the commonest type of fault necessitating a service call. Although they are a tribute to the reliability of modern equipment, the replies were unexpectedly and completely unanimous: failure by the user to study the operating instructions carefully enough. Later another well-known manufacturer put it differently: '60% of all our service calls are now due to finger trouble'. It has to be admitted that some *User's Manuals* are heavier going than others but the users nevertheless have a duty to persevere with them. A 'dummy run' can help to ease the task.

Dummy run

The first sea voyage with a new receiver is not the best occasion on which to start finding one's way around the keyboard of a position fixing receiver but it appears that people sometimes do this and then complain when something unaccountable happens. A very real merit of the DR facility is its ability to help a prospective user to become familiar with much of the operating procedure before going to sea, and indeed in the comfort of home if a suitable power supply can be found. No antenna is required. The bleeper in some receivers may protest at the lack of radio signals but there is generally a procedural way round that.

Once the latitude and longitude of a starting position have been entered, keying in a speed and heading will get the notional craft under way and the lat/long display of present position will start to change accordingly. The craft can be steered by keying in new headings and if waypoints have been entered the steering displays can be observed under dynamic conditions. Facilities such as waypoint-approach alarms and ETAs can be exercised and so far as the processor is concerned the illusion of reality is total (within the confines of the DR mode). The user can add to the realism by choosing a starting position on a familiar chart and placing waypoints at appropriate positions.

At present the type of DR facility needed for this exercise is found mainly on the more expensive receivers. Adding it to the simpler designs would involve little change in the software, and none in hardware if provision is already made for entering heading and speed from the keyboard. Perhaps it is not too much to hope that this kind of 'built-in familiarisation' will come to be ranked with built-in test as essential for position fixing equipment.

Index